VOL TWO / ISSUE TWO
MEDICAL
FRONTIERS

NEW SCIENTIST
THE COLLECTION
110 High Holborn,
London WC1V 6EU
+44 (0)20 7611 1202
enquiries@newscientist.com

Editor-in-chief Graham Lawton
Editor Julia Brown
Art editor Craig Mackie
Picture editor Prue Waller
Subeditor Richard Lim
Graphics Dave Johnston
Production editor Mick O'Hare
Project manager Henry Gomm
Publisher John MacFarlane

© 2015 Reed Business
Information Ltd, England
New Scientist The Collection is
published four times per year by
Reed Business Information Ltd
ISSN 2054-6386

Printed in England by Precision
Colour Printing, Telford,
Shropshire, and distributed by
Marketforce UK Ltd
+44 (0)20 3148 3333
Display advertising
+44 (0)20 7611 1291
displayads@newscientist.com

Cover image
Simon Danaher

Tomorrow's medicine today

AT THE beginning of the 20th century, medicine was still more art than science. Penicillin was decades off, surgery crude, immunisation rare, cancer a death sentence and blood transfusions were thought impossible. Even in affluent countries, two-thirds of people died before they were 60.

Then came the first world war. As a result of its horrors, new fronts opened up in medical research. Trauma surgery, infection control, transfusions and vaccination were all revolutionised, and scientific medicine as we know it was born.

These areas are still undergoing radical developments. And many other medical frontiers have also opened up, transforming our health in ways that would have been unimaginable back then. Life expectancy in the West is now more than 80, and there is every reason to believe it can keep rising.

This sixth issue of *New Scientist: The Collection* is dedicated to the cutting edge of medical innovation, from before birth to end-of-life care.

It is a journey that often takes us to unexpected places. In the search for new drugs and treatments, this compilation of classic articles from *New Scientist* travels to the top of Everest, the bottom of the deepest ocean trenches and to the jungles and deserts where snakes, scorpions and toxic lizards are giving up their medical secrets.

In the laboratory, there has been a revolution in DNA sequencing, body parts are being built from scratch, and stem cells look so promising that we have made them the focus of a brand new article (see page 71).

Not every advance has meant doing more, though. Sometimes it pays to step back and let nature – or evolution – take its course.

Research never stops, but this collection will give you a snapshot of the dazzling array of advances happening right now.

Chapter 1 starts at the beginning: diagnosis, where technical advances have transformed our ability to work out what's wrong.

Finding a disease means fighting it, and Chapter 2 looks at some new strategies at our disposal, from vaccines with extra benefits to ways to eradicate disease completely.

Treatment often means drugs, and Chapter 3 joins the hunt for new ones, from discovering them at the bottom of the sea to growing them in carrot cells and even extracting them from radioactive scorpions.

Chapter 4 reports from the front line of another war, exploring ways to stop cancer cells in their tracks by ambushing them, enlisting gut bacteria or maybe by "printing" bespoke antidotes.

Chapter 5 moves on to our capacity for regeneration. We can now change the body's source code and reprogram cells, sometimes before a person is even born. It also examines prospects for building whole organs.

Modern medicine really comes into its own in life-or-death situations, and Chapter 6 is about advances in emergency care. In surgery, too, doctors are refining their approach and swapping the knife for a beam of sound.

The body would be nothing without the brain. The discoveries in Chapter 7 could erase your fears, alter your memories or spark your nerves into surprising action.

Finally, Chapter 8 enters medicine's latest frontier: the digital world. Apps, virtual reality and computing power are changing medicine in ways unimaginable even a few years ago. Here's a glimpse of what medicine will look like in the future.

Julia Brown, Editor

CONTENTS

NewScientist
THE COLLECTION

CONTRIBUTORS

Sally Adee
is a feature editor at *New Scientist*

Michael Brooks
is a science writer and *New Scientist* consultant

Andy Coghlan
is a news reporter at *New Scientist*

David Cohen
is a junior doctor in Bristol, UK

Moheb Costandi
is a science writer based in London

Paul Davies
is principal investigator at the Center for Convergence of Physical Science and Cancer Biology at Arizona State University

Catherine de Lange
is a feature editor at *New Scientist*

Ed Douglas
is a writer based in Sheffield, UK

Linda Geddes
is a *New Scientist* consultant based in Bristol, UK

Jessica Hamzelou
is a news reporter at *New Scientist*

Hal Hodson
is a technology reporter at *New Scientist*

Bob Holmes
is a consultant for *New Scientist* based in Edmonton, Canada

Christian Jobin
is a professor of medicine at the University of Florida in Gainesville

Dan Jones
is a writer based in Brighton, UK

Phil McKenna
is a writer based in Cambridge, Massachusetts

Debora MacKenzie
is a consultant for *New Scientist* based in Brussels

James Mitchell Crow
is deputy editor of Cosmos magazine

Samantha Murphy
is a journalist based in Lancaster, Pennsylvania

Tiffany O'Callaghan
is a senior opinion editor at *New Scientist*

Helen Pilcher
is a freelance writer based in the UK

Meera Senthilingam
is a global health writer, broadcaster and consultant based in London

Frank Swain
is communities editor at *New Scientist*

Dick Teresi
is a writer based in Amherst, Massachusetts

Helen Thomson
is a science writer based in London

Jon White
is an opinion editor at *New Scientist*

Clare Wilson
is a news reporter at *New Scientist*

With the exception of "Miracle cells", which is new to this collection, the articles here were first published in *New Scientist* between February 2010 and October 2014. They have been updated and revised.

VOL TWO / ISSUE TWO
MEDICAL FRONTIERS

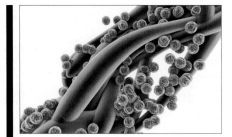

1

Diagnosis

6   What's eating you?
10   Written in blood
13   The germ detectives

2

Fighting infection

16   Every last trace
20   I must cheat
23   The mark of noro
26   Small shot, big impact
30   Breath of fresh air

3
Drug hunting

34 Panacea
38 Cure-all no more
42 Drugs with bite
46 Going to extremes
50 Field of dreams

4
Cancer

54 The cruellest cut?
58 Fatal attraction
62 What's really going on in those cancer cells?
64 Print a virus to kill the cancer
66 Time to enlist life-saving, gutsy allies

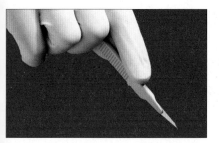

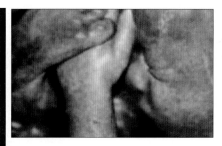

5
Regeneration

68 Healed in the womb
71 Miracle cells
74 Let's get physical
78 Heart, heal thyself
82 Rebuild your body

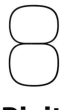

6
Emergency room

86 Surgery's new sound
90 Darwin's doctor
94 Code red
98 Resurrection man
100 Out of thin air

7
Brains and wiring

104 Erase your fear...
108 The vital spark
112 The memory fix

8
Digital doctor

118 The doctor is in your pocket
122 The virtual therapist will see you now
124 In sickness and in health

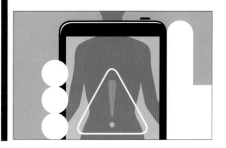

ALL PAPER IS NOT CREATED EQUAL.

Especially in business, looking good on paper really matters. ColorLok® Technology gives paper more vivid colours, bolder blacks, and faster drying times.* So make a strong impression by choosing paper with the ColorLok logo. **Learn more at colorlok.com**

THE SCIENCE OF WOWING YOUR CUSTOMERS

ColorLok Technology turns everyday office paper into your canvas for eye-popping imagery and incredibly professional presentations. How? By injecting additives during the paper-making process that enable the paper to "lock" pigments at the surface. Without this technology, paper acts more like a sponge, absorbing black and colour pigments deep into the fibres of the paper and away from the surface.

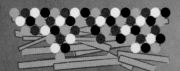

Without ColorLok Technology, pigment sinks deep into the paper's fibres. Black appears duller and colours less vibrant.

When you print on paper with ColorLok Technology, the additives within the paper react with the pigments, keeping colour near the surface for bold, vivid results.

A NEW LOOK FOR ECO-FRIENDLY PAPER

Even recyclable paper looks better than ever, because ColorLok Technology creates a shield between the surface and subsurface fibres. Printouts on recycled paper can now retain a brighter, richer appearance, so you can be eco-friendly without compromising quality. What's more, paper with ColorLok Technology is actually easier to recycle. So yes, you can look good and do good.

VIVID COLOURS

Richer, brighter
images and graphics
on all your printers

BOLDER BLACKS

Means crisper, sharper
text and lines than with
standard paper

FASTER DRYING

Less smear and faster
handling compared
to papers without
ColorLok Technology

ECO-FRIENDLY

Easier to recycle,
with results that
don't look dull

CONSISTENCY

Consistent and reliable
printing regardless of
which machine is used

FASTER DRYING · BOLDER BLACKS · VIVID COLORS ®

ColorLok
TECHNOLOGY

What's eating you?

Superfast tests for microbes
could save thousands of lives.
Debora MacKenzie reports

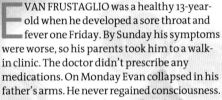

EVAN FRUSTAGLIO was a healthy 13-year-old when he developed a sore throat and fever one Friday. By Sunday his symptoms were worse, so his parents took him to a walk-in clinic. The doctor didn't prescribe any medications. On Monday Evan collapsed in his father's arms. He never regained consciousness.

It turned out he had swine flu, which was widespread at the time. The drug Tamiflu might well have saved him.

This case was not a one-off. Every day millions of people go to clinics and hospitals seeking treatment for some kind of infectious disease. Most often these are respiratory infections, and their symptoms can be identical whatever bacterium or virus is to blame. Usually the best doctors can do is make an educated guess about which bug is responsible. In many cases it doesn't actually matter if they get it wrong, because our immune systems will kill off the offending bug.

But it can matter a lot. Not only are life-threatening infections sometimes missed, but even when it is clear that someone's life is in danger, it can take days or even weeks to identify the cause. The delay means that a person might not get treatment that could have saved them.

For example, it is thought that many of the 250,000 people who die of blood poisoning in the US each year could be saved if the bacterium responsible were identified and appropriate treatment given early. On the other hand, giving antibiotics encourages antibiotic-resistant superbugs to emerge – and thus harms people indirectly.

It doesn't have to be this way, not any more. We can now take a swab of, say, someone's throat and identify within hours which viruses and bacteria are present. Devices capable of identifying bugs quickly and cheaply could save thousands of lives if widely used. Not only would they help ensure people get appropriate treatment fast, but they would also allow dangerous new pathogens to be spotted much more quickly and encourage

companies to develop treatments. So why isn't the technology being adopted?

Part of the problem is that the whole culture of diagnosing infection is rooted in just that – culture. "For 150 years until recently, the only way to diagnose anything was to put your sample in a jar of warm soup and wait for something to grow," says David Ecker of Ibis Biosciences, a diagnostics company owned by pharmaceutical giant Abbott.

Some germs just won't grow in culture, and those that do take a while to incubate – anything from three days to weeks in the case of TB. And the approach is far from foolproof: the standard culture test for the most common toxic *E. coli* strain would have missed the kind behind the outbreak in Germany that recently killed nearly 50 people and cost farmers hundreds of millions of euros. A better, faster test might have saved lives and livelihoods.

More flexible tests

There are already faster tests around. Over the past decade, many new dipsticks have become available that change colour to signal when specific molecules are present, just as in pregnancy tests. They have one major limitation, though. "They're great at detecting the antibodies a patient makes to an infection, but those don't appear for weeks, a bit late for many diseases," says Rosanna Peeling, head of diagnostics at the London School of Hygiene and Tropical Medicine. "What we really want is something like the tricorder on *Star Trek*. You could point it at anything and it would say what it was" (see "The doctor is in your pocket", page 118).

Thanks to the revolution in DNA technology, devices that work a bit like that already exist. They have yet to reach hospitals, though. At the moment, the diagnostic DNA tests hospitals use look for just one kind of virus or bacterium. They use a method called PCR to reveal whether a specific sequence is present in a sample. This is useful if you already know what ❯

ALFRED PASIEKA/SPL

the patient has and you want to see whether a treatment is working, for instance. But it is not great at identifying the cause of an infection. Carrying out dozens of separate DNA tests is prohibitively expensive – and there are around 1400 different kinds of viruses and bacteria that can infect people.

The other obvious problem with single tests is that they can only find the germ they are designed to detect. Yet in cases of flu, for instance, secondary bacterial infections can be lethal. So Ian Lipkin of Columbia University in New York has developed a variant of PCR called MassTag that can look for up to 30 different sequences, and thus up to 30 bugs at once.

Unfortunately, it is less sensitive than testing for a single sequence. As a result, while MassTag and tests like it have been approved for monitoring the spread of infections in the community, they are not yet approved for diagnosing individual patients. "The US Food and Drug Administration won't approve it if it is less sensitive than the standard, single PCR, despite its greater breadth," Lipkin says.

That greater breadth is needed. Joseph DeRisi of the University of California, San Francisco, tells of a 28-year-old woman who went to hospital coughing up phlegm and blood. Soon she was fighting for her life on a respirator. No positive results came out of $100,000 worth of tests; no cultures, even of lung tissue, grew anything. DNA tests for 28 pathogens came up negative.

After a week, desperate doctors sent DeRisi a sample. His team has developed a wide-ranging test using a microarray – a slide with strands of viral DNA, termed probes, attached to it. The sample is washed over it and any DNA in the sample that matches a probe will bind to it.

An early version of DeRisi's Virochip helped identify a new kind of coronavirus as the cause of SARS. The latest version has 60,000 probes from more than 1500 viruses. Lipkin has developed a similar array, the GreeneChip, that also looks for bacterial, fungal and parasite DNA.

In a few hours, the Virochip came up with an answer – the woman had the parainfluenza 4 virus. Because it usually causes only mild colds, there are no standard tests for it and, as with most viruses, no treatments. The woman eventually fought it off.

In this case, then, identifying the pathogen did not help. The woman was even given antibiotics as a precaution despite the evidence that a virus was responsible. "It would be a brave clinician who withheld antibiotics from a patient on a respirator just because a particular virus was discovered," says Graham Cooke of Imperial College London.

Of course, the test might have been a lifesaver had it revealed an infection for which we have a treatment. What's more, if such testing becomes routine, it will give companies a reason to develop treatments – you cannot sell drugs against a particular pathogen if there is no way to tell who is infected in time for the treatment to make difference. But testing will only become routine if the tests are cheap and easy to perform. So far both DeRisi's and Lipkin's arrays require complicated processing and take 12 to 24 hours to give a result.

Those working on microarray-based tests believe they can be made cheaper and quicker. So far, though, they are working to get regulatory approval, which at the moment comes at the expense of breadth. A handful of microarrays have been approved in the US and Europe, each able to identify around 10 or 20 pathogens. It is not clear if really big arrays that can identify rare or novel pathogens will ever overcome the technological and regulatory hurdles needed to reach the clinic. The FDA has not even told companies what evidence it needs to approve such devices for clinical use, says Charles Chiu, who works with DeRisi on the Virochip. In theory, the sensitivity and specificity of each probe needs to be tested, but this is impossible with tens of thousands of probes.

Although big arrays cannot be used for routine diagnosis, they can be used to solve occasional medical mysteries, reveal what pathogens are circulating and screen blood or drugs. Yet even the biggest arrays don't always produce an answer. When Lipkin used GreeneChip to try to find out what had killed three people who all received organ

"Twice we've identified a new disease – swine flu and the cause of SARS. It wasn't a drill, it was the real deal"

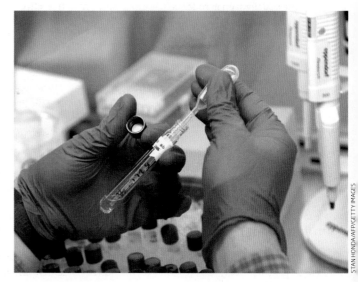

Existing DNA tests are fine if you know what you are looking for

STAN HONDA/AFP/GETTY IMAGES

Some airports scanned for fevers during the swine flu pandemic

RAMZI HAIDAR/AFP/GETTY IMAGES

transplants from the same donor, it found no matches.

Lipkin then resorted to sequencing all the RNA in samples from one victim, yielding 100,000 sequences in all. Heavy-duty computer processing revealed that 14 of them came from a new arenavirus, a kind of virus more usually seen in rodents.

This "sequence everything" approach, known as metagenomics, had previously been used to identify which viruses and bacteria lurk in seawater, for instance, but until recently it was far too time-consuming and expensive to be worth considering when looking for the cause of diseases. The beauty of the approach, though, is that it can reveal in glorious detail exactly which microbes are present, even if they are unlike anything seen before. In the case of bacteria, it can even reveal which genes conferring resistance to antibiotics are present and thus which antibiotics won't work. And the technology is advancing fast: "I think we are maybe five years from the point where we could use sequencing for routine pathogen diagnosis," says Chiu (see "The germ detectives", page 13). "The question now is

whether we will go to microarray first, or just straight to that."

Or maybe another method will beat them both. "Sequencing isn't fast and cheap enough yet," says Ecker of Ibis Biosciences, which has developed a device called IRIDICA. "Our machine costs $400,000, but each test costs little, so it's effective for a big hospital lab," he said soon after it was developed.

It works by making lots of copies of any DNA characteristic of a wide range of viruses, bacteria or fungi. Then a mass spectrometer determines the mass of the amplified DNA fragments, which varies depending on their length and composition. The result is a library of characteristic molecular fingerprints that can be used to identify the pathogen – even if the disease it causes has not been seen before.

In 2003, the company also correctly identified a kind of coronavirus as the cause of SARS. In 2009, it spotted a new flu virus in a boy at the US-Mexican border – the first diagnosis of swine flu in the US. "That's twice we've identified a new disease when it wasn't a drill, it was the real deal," says Ecker. To impress the FDA, IRIDICA must prove its technique is as good as culturing the

pathogen, which remains the gold standard. "The trouble is, we're more sensitive," says Ecker. When IRIDICA finds pathogens in a sample and culturing doesn't, Ecker must prove his machine has got it right.

"Introducing a game-changing technology is always going to take time," says Ecker. So far, the company has approval in the European Union to diagnose sepsis and is pursuing approval in the US for this and hundreds of other infections. Yet that is far less than the technology can do – and falls short of what is needed. What's more, if the technology does take off, costs could come down to the point that smaller hospitals and labs could afford it.

Will doctors want it? Some might see such tests as a threat, but they are no replacement for doctors. "We'll still need their judgement based on the patient's history and symptoms," Ecker says. Tests may identify a microbe that isn't the cause of the disease or it might pick up several, only one of which is problematic. And diagnosis is just the start of treatment.

Chiu is optimistic about the prospects for the technology. "The new generation of medics is tech-savvy," he says. "Medicine is crying out for this: if it works, they'll want it." ∎

A single drop of your blood can reveal all kinds of deeply personal information about your lifestyle and your past. **Helen Pilcher** reports

Written in your blood

B ORN into a working-class family, "Olivia" was abused as a child. Her parents were emotionally distant and offered her little comfort. Now aged 56, Olivia lives near a busy road. She is poor, smokes, drinks much more than is good for her, and has panic attacks.

If Olivia really existed, she probably wouldn't want many people to know all these details about her life – but a tiny drop of her blood could give it all away. The technology now exists to read in our blood all the kinds of information described above, and more. Such tests could tell others much about our health and habits, state of mind and socio-economic status. It could also reveal details from bygone decades, such as experiences from the furthest recesses of our childhood.

This is possible because the world we live in and the experiences we have leave subtle traces on our DNA, and we are now learning how to decipher these marks. On the positive side, this powerful tool could help doctors spot all kinds of diseases and disorders. It could also help police create a comprehensive profile of a suspect from a single drop of blood at a crime scene.

But as the law stands, there is nothing to prevent such tests being used by unscrupulous insurers, employers and even journalists. Would you want anyone to be able to read your life story, one you are potentially giving away whenever you have a blood test or throw a bloody tissue in the bin?

It is already possible to learn a fair amount about a person from a drop of their blood, by looking at the sequence of their DNA. This can reveal your sex and ethnic background, and give a pretty good idea of your hair colour, eye colour and even skin colour. It can also hint at more personal things, such as whether you are a risk-taker, an early bird or have a behavioural disorder such as ADHD.

But who we are isn't written in our genes. The stuff that really matters is the result of our lifestyles, experiences and environment. You might think this doesn't have anything to do with our DNA. In fact, all kinds of labels get attached to the DNA in our cells as we go through life.

The most common form of labelling involves attaching a methyl group to one of the DNA letters. Methylation doesn't alter the underlying sequence, but it can shut down nearby genes. If you think of our DNA as a recipe book for making a human, then the methyl groups are like yellow stickies saying "don't make this". Some recipes have no stickies on them, while others end up plastered with them.

The vast majority of these labels get added as we laze in our mother's womb, and shortly after. This is when cells are taking on specialised roles, and methylation helps switch off genes that aren't needed, ensuring that a liver cell doesn't express nerve cell genes, for example.

The upshot is that if you take cells of the same type from different individuals and compare the pattern of labels on the DNA – the epigenome – there will be many similarities. Many epigenetic changes are genetically

MR R. SMITH
AGE: 35
SMOKER
LOVING PARENTS
ABUSED AS A CHILD
LIVES NEAR A BUSY ROAD
LOW SOCIO-ECONOMIC STATU
EXPOSED TO PESTICIDES
EXPOSED TO ARSENIC

LOT 1404090711

REF R7552

programmed. But there are tens of millions of sites in the genome where methylation can occur, and no two individuals will have exactly the same pattern. This variation between individuals is at least partly to do with our lifestyles, and can therefore reveal much about our life history. "The epigenome is a snapshot of the major events in your life," says Tim Spector of King's College London.

By looking at epigenetic marks, Spector can tell if someone is a smoker, an ex-smoker or has hardly ever taken a drag. He can tell if someone has, or has ever had, cancer. "You can even get an idea of what they eat," he says. And because we accrue epigenetic changes throughout life, the marks can also reveal our age.

Exposure to substances such as diesel fumes, pesticides and arsenic also produces distinct patterns. Analyse the epigenome, then, and you might be able to work out what chemicals a person has been exposed to, perhaps even where they have been.

This would have been unthinkable just a few years ago, when detecting methylation patterns was difficult and expensive. But the technology has advanced at an incredible pace. It is now possible, for instance, to buy a $200 off-the-shelf "chip" that shows which of 450,000 sites in the genome are methylated.

Window to your past

With the help of such tools, researchers have begun looking for correlations between methylation patterns and particular environments or experiences. All kinds of cells are being looked at, but blood cells are the most common, as they are easy to obtain. The last few years have seen a flood of studies highlighting patterns related to everything from suicide to success in dieting.

One US study in 2013 asked its 1000 or so participants to rate their wealth by ticking which of four assets – car, house, land and financial investments – they owned. The richest people had different methylation patterns to the poorest. Epigenetic differences have also been spotted between the most and least socially privileged in the UK city of Glasgow. "There are clear signals that the epigenome is being affected by socially patterned factors," says Ana Diez-Roux of the Drexel University School of Public Health in Philadelphia, Pennsylvania,

KEVIN CURTIS/SCIENCE PHOTO LIBRARY

who co-authored the US study.

The epigenome may even be a window to episodes from our distant past. Holocaust survivors have very different methylation patterns to people who haven't had a severe traumatic experience, for instance. Adults with post-traumatic stress disorder (PTSD) also carry unusual profiles. It appears that

"The epigenome is a snapshot of life events. You can even get an idea of what someone eats"

traumatic life experiences leave epigenetic marks long after physical scars have faded.

Among people with PTSD, the altered marks are more pronounced in those who were abused as children than those who were traumatised as adults, a study in 2013 found. "So there may be a trauma-prone period during childhood," says study author Elisabeth Binder from the Max-Planck Institute of Psychiatry in Munich, Germany.

Quite how people end up with these different patterns is unclear. Nor is it known what, if any, effect they have. Some of the variations in methylation could be in regions of DNA that don't do anything important. Other variations may impinge on key genes.

For instance, Binder suspects some of the epigenetic changes associated with trauma during childhood increase levels of hormones called glucocorticoids, involved in the stress response. This probably makes it harder for abused children to cope with stress later in life, and more vulnerable to conditions such as PTSD and schizophrenia as adults.

If you just want to use epigenetic patterns to reveal someone's life history, though, it isn't necessary to understand how the variations come about or how they affect a person. All that matters is that the patterns exist. "Epigenetic marks show a lot of promise as biomarkers," says Adrian Bird of the Wellcome Trust Centre for Cell Biology in Edinburgh, UK. The issue is how reliable they are, he says. The studies done so far have only involved small numbers of people and have used disparate methods. "It's difficult to base predictive science on them at the moment," Bird says.

The situation echoes the early days of cheap DNA testing, when tens of thousands of potential biomarkers based on single DNA letter changes were highlighted by small-scale studies. Most results couldn't be replicated. But larger, better-implemented studies ❯

WIPING THE SLATE CLEAN

Subtle traces on your DNA can reveal what's happened to you during your lifetime (see main story). Although the vast majority of studies have focused on negative life experiences such as childhood abuse, this kind of testing doesn't have to be all doom and gloom.

Positive experiences alter our epigenome as well. "Positive events can change you every bit as much as negative ones," says Rachel Yehuda, a clinical neuroscientist at Mount Sinai Hospital, New York. "Biology doesn't discriminate between the two."

At least some changes to the epigenome are reversible. So when epigenetic marks, as they are known, turn out to have undesirable consequences, we can try to change them. A handful of drugs that affect DNA methylation already exist, and are being used to treat cancers in which faulty gene labelling plays a role. But even things as simple as diet, meditation or counselling should alter the epigenome too.

Yehuda has been looking at combat veterans with PTSD. In a small preliminary study, she showed that psychotherapy, the first line of treatment for PTSD, can alter the activity of a stress hormone by altering the methylation of a specific region of DNA. What's more, the methylation status of another region seems to predict whether people will respond to psychotherapy or not.

So epigenetics can not only help us tell what's wrong with someone, it may also reveal the best way to treat them and help check how effective that treatment has been.

As yet, it remains unclear to what extent the epigenome can be rewritten. Do telltale traces of major life events persist until death? Or can all changes be reversed, meaning there's a limit to what epigenetics tests can tell us about people's pasts?

We don't yet know the answer, but it is already clear that to a large extent our epigenetic narratives are not cast in stone. We don't just write our epigenetic story - we have the power to edit it too.

have turned up reliable biomarkers.

"We have to learn from that," says epigenetics researcher Stephan Beck of the University College London Cancer Institute. "The studies need to be massively scaled up. Only then will we see how reliable the markers are." However, epigeneticists are hopeful that even if many of the patterns discovered so far do fall by the wayside, some will prove resilient and many more will be discovered.

The level of detail encoded in these patterns also remains uncertain. Will an epigenetic test give us only a summary of our life story – like chapter headings in an autobiography – or can it tell us more? For instance, although a person's methylation profile can show whether they experienced something very stressful as a child, it cannot tell us what that was – at least, not yet. As we learn more, we may be able to read finer details. "We need to better understand which environments leave which marks," says Binder.

We also need to start thinking about the implications. As yet, no one has looked for multiple epigenetic patterns within the same person, but there's no reason why it can't be done. One blood sample and one chip could yield enough information to scan for thousands of methylation signatures, revealing a wealth of information about someone's current lifestyle and their past.

To investigators trying to identify someone based only on blood from a crime scene, this will be of great interest. In some countries, police are already using genetic tests that predict hair and eye colour, for instance. Add in epigenetic clues to someone's age, social status and even where they live, and investigators could get a much better idea of who they are looking for.

Epigenetic tests may also be able to tell whether someone has taken illegal drugs or violated a drinking ban. In some countries, various kinds of tests are already being used to monitor illegal drug use or enforce compliance, such as anklets that measure blood alcohol. If they prove reliable, epigenetic tests could become part of this toolkit, although such evidence is unlikely to be admissible in court any time soon.

Methylation patterns have also been linked to numerous diseases, including diabetes, and to psychiatric disorders such as depression. In theory, a single, cheap blood test could reveal not only the state of your health but also your medical history and maybe your medical future. Spector, for example, has identified a methylation profile involving around 400 sites that can, he claims, give five years' warning of the onset of breast cancer.

While epigenetic profiling could be a powerful tool for catching criminals and saving lives, there are, as ever, potential dangers. What if you had episodes in your past you wanted to hide? You might not worry about your doctor having access to your epigenome, but what about your life insurance company? Could they increase your premiums or refuse to insure you on the basis of what your epigenetic profile reveals? How would you like your employer or school to get their hands on this information?

"There's a whole host of legal and ethical issues surrounding epigenetics," says bioethicist Mark Rothstein of the University of Louisville School of Medicine in Kentucky, "but people are ignoring them for reasons I just don't understand."

In the UK and some US states, it is illegal to analyse someone's DNA without their consent, but there's nothing to stop you analysing their epigenome. It's a similar story with discrimination by employers and insurers. The UK and the US have laws addressing genetic discrimination. "But there are no specific laws for epigenetics," says Rothstein. "It's very alarming."

Rothstein thinks we need to ban non-consensual epigenetic testing. Then we can start to think about the beneficial uses of these tests, and build up the legislation around them. There's a whole debate to be had. "We need to get it started." ∎

The germ detectives

Deadly microbes have no place to hide when the gene police are on the case. **Linda Geddes** investigates

THEY were some of the most vulnerable patients in the hospital: newborn babies, many of them premature, or with other problems that meant they needed to stay in the special care baby unit at Addenbrooke's Hospital in Cambridge, UK. The infants were hooked up to machines via a tangle of tubes and wires that supplied oxygen, food and fluids and monitored their vital signs to keep them safe. Yet now they faced a new hazard: hospital superbug MRSA.

This form of the bacterium, *Staphylococcus aureus*, can be a deadly menace thanks to a mutation that gives it resistance to the main antibiotic used to treat it, methicillin. In mid-2011, MRSA was found on the skin of three infants in the special care baby unit at Addenbrooke's. While its presence wasn't yet making the babies ill, the bacterium could find its way into their bodies and trigger a life-threatening infection.

The staff had to take action. The babies were lifted from their cribs and their bodies carefully washed all over. Even the insides of their nostrils were gently dabbed with antimicrobial lotion.

While this was going on, the ward was closed for several days, and everything in it thoroughly disinfected, from the ventilation machines down to the thermometers. "A deep clean is very disruptive," says Estée Török, an infectious disease specialist at Addenbrooke's. "It's not something we take lightly."

Four days later, the doctors learned that their efforts had been in vain: the superbug had been found on yet another baby's skin. Where could it be coming from? If they didn't find out soon, babies' lives would be in jeopardy.

When details of the cases landed on the desk of Simon Harris at the Sanger Institute several miles down the road, he felt he could help. Harris's team had recently reported on a way that genetic testing could be used to investigate just this kind of outbreak.

Their paper had described how the team investigated an MRSA outbreak in a hospital in Thailand, several years earlier, using stored samples from patients. By sequencing bacterial DNA from the samples, they had tracked how the infection had spread through the hospital, from patient to patient.

Harris had pointed out that, given the staggering improvements in the speed and cost of the technology involved, it was now possible to a sequence a bacterium's entire genome – its full set of genes – overnight. Genome sequencing could be used as a tool to investigate a live outbreak, he argued, and maybe even halt it.

Now the team had the chance to put their plan into action at a hospital on their own doorstep. Armed with a desktop DNA sequencing machine, Harris was about to test his mettle as a germ detective.

The first time microbial genetics was used to investigate the spread of disease was in 1990. Kimberly Bergalis, a 21-year-old from Florida, had developed AIDS although she'd never had sex or injected drugs. When HIV experts at the US Centers for Disease Control (CDC) heard about the case, they were alarmed that there might be a new way for the virus ❯

KELLY DYSON

"Genomic sequencing was used to work out whether the new strain of flu had the potential to trigger a global pandemic"

to spread, so they dispatched two investigators to her house to interview her. Yet it was Bergalis's mother, a local healthcare worker, who came up with the best lead: she discovered that her daughter's dentist had pneumonia, which can be associated with AIDS. It turned out that he, too, was HIV-positive.

Of course, that was no proof he was the source of Bergalis's infection. To investigate further, the CDC used DNA sequencing, then in its infancy, to compare a single HIV gene in samples taken from Bergalis, her dentist, and other infected people in the US.

Viruses are constantly mutating and evolving as they pass from person to person, which provides a way to track their spread: the more genetically related two people's viruses are, the more likely it is that one person caught the virus from the other. In this case, the samples from Bergalis and her dentist were more closely related than those from the general population, suggesting that the dentist had given Bergalis HIV, or vice versa. For the CDC that discovery confirmed that there was no new route for transmitting what was then an inevitably fatal infection.

Genetic testing has since been used in many other cases of HIV transmission, often where the transmitter is accused of acting recklessly. The ethics of prosecuting such cases may be debatable – critics say this approach could put people off getting tested for HIV. But as the technology has advanced, genetic testing of microbes has found wider uses.

Going cheap

The cost of DNA sequencing has plummeted since its inception

Cost per 1000 bases of DNA ($)

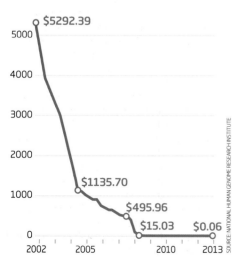

$5292.39

$1135.70

$495.96

$15.03

$0.06

SOURCE: NATIONAL HUMAN GENOME RESEARCH INSTITUTE

While most technologies get cheaper and better over time, the rate of progress of DNA sequencing has outstripped even advances in computing (see diagram, below). The first draft of the human genome, for instance, took 13 years to complete and cost $3 billion. Today, anyone can have their personal genome sequenced in 24 hours, for a few thousand dollars.

Viral and bacterial genomes, which have far less DNA than our own, are even cheaper to sequence than those of humans. That makes it feasible to start sequencing samples from many patients and getting the results back overnight. And that, Harris had realised, could allow real-time tracking of how an infection spreads.

Disease outbreaks are normally investigated by sending out staff to the place where people are getting sick and grilling patients face to face about where they've been and who they've been in contact with. For this reason, it's often called shoe-leather epidemiology. Doctors are looking for links in time and place between people infected by the microbe in question. "It's hugely laborious and expensive," says Oliver Pybus, who studies viral evolution at the University of Oxford.

Genome sequencing, on the other hand, should be faster as well as more accurate. After all, connecting two cases because both people ate at the same restaurant one night is what police call circumstantial evidence; connecting them because their microbes are genetically related provides more certainty.

When the first cases of swine flu in people broke out in Mexico in early 2009, Pybus was one of a team of virologists that used genomic sequencing to track the evolution of the virus. "It was the first major outbreak of the post-genomic era," he says. "Large numbers of viral genomes were generated and shared online in real time as the pandemic unfolded."

In the case of swine flu, the disease's origins were already known: it had crossed over to humans from pigs and was now being transmitted between people (see also "What's eating you?", page 6). But genomic sequencing could also be used to work out how fast flu was spreading between people, and so whether it had the potential to trigger a global pandemic. This was vital information for doctors around the world.

The team calculated that each case of swine flu was being transmitted, on average, to 1.2 other people, a relatively low figure compared with the 1918 flu pandemic, say. And the figure fitted broadly with the estimates of the shoe-leather epidemiologists:

Vulnerable: newborn babies and superbugs are not a good mix

they had come up with a rate of between 1.4 and 1.6 transmissions per case. "They were independent sources of info, and they corroborated each other, which is strong evidence you've got it right," Pybus says. "We proved it was possible to do the genetic stuff in real time alongside the traditional analysis."

But as the outbreak of MRSA at Addenbrooke's was about to show, genome sequencing sometimes comes up with different answers to traditional methods.

Compared with viruses, bacteria are much bigger beasts, both physically and in terms of the amount of DNA in their genomes. HIV, for example, has nine genes, while MRSA has about 2800. But in the past few years, overnight sequencing of even a bacterial genome has come within our grasp.

It only costs about £95 to sequence the complete genome of one person's MRSA sample, for instance. Even if dozens of samples need testing, that is small change compared with the cost of an outbreak that might keep patients in hospital for weeks, perhaps needing intensive care.

Widening the net

When Harris was called in to help, the first thing he did was to ask for samples from any previous cases of MRSA that had cropped up in the special care baby unit over the past six months. There had been 17 such cases, appearing in three distinct clusters that the hospital's microbiologists had concluded were unconnected. But all they'd had to go on was the standard method of taking samples from patients, growing them in the lab, and testing them to see which antibiotics they are resistant to. The pattern of antibiotic resistance can indicate how related different samples are, but it is not infallible.

Indeed, as it turned out, in this case the standard method had given a wrong steer. The more accurate genome-sequencing method showed that all but three of the cases were related, Harris was able to tell the doctors.

But there was a problem: the timing of the infections didn't make sense. "You'd expect to have an infected person who overlaps with another infected person," says Harris. "But here we had three clusters, separated by 17 and 33 days. A month is quite a long time to have no cases and for it to reappear."

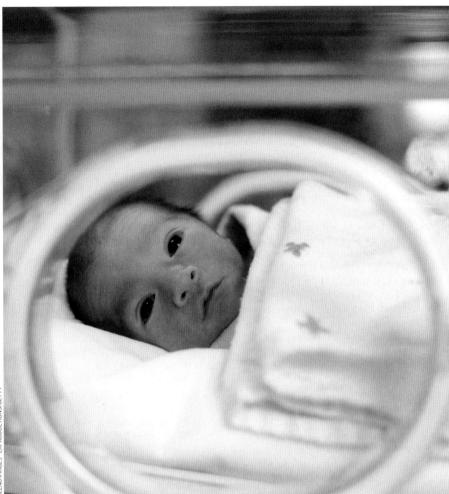

Something else had to be going on. So the team widened its net, searching for other cases of MRSA within the hospital and local community, and found another 10 cases that Harris showed were genetically related.

Suspiciously, all had a link to the special babies ward at the hospital. Five of the cases were new mums with abscesses in their breasts. One needed surgery because the infection was out of control. Others had turned up at their local doctor's surgery with painful pustules on their legs or ears. A bit of digging – back to shoe-leather epidemiology again – showed that almost all had some connection to the special babies unit, for instance, having been in the maternity ward at the same time as parents of babies in the unit.

For a while it all went quiet, with no further cases of MRSA at Addenbrooke's for 64 days. But then alarm bells rang again: another baby in the special babies unit tested positive. The investigation had transformed from a retrospective study into a real-time one.

Bacteria taken from the baby were sequenced overnight. "By 10 am the following morning I had analysed the data and could confirm to the hospital that the new case

was linked to the outbreak," says Harris.

As it seemed unlikely that the bacteria had survived the deep clean and then persisted on hospital equipment for two months, the evidence pointed to the same MRSA strain being repeatedly introduced into the hospital by a healthy carrier of the bacteria. That was plausible as nearly three people in every 100 have MRSA on their skin without suffering ill effects.

If a healthcare worker was carrying the bug, the situation would have to be handled sensitively to avoid apportioning blame. But with the genetic evidence so strong, Addenbrooke's now felt able to ask its staff if they would volunteer for testing. Of the 152 staff who came forward, one tested positive for MRSA that was genetically related to the other cases. Sure enough, it was someone who frequently visited the special baby unit.

Fortunately this was a simple problem to address. The staff member, who has remained anonymous, was prescribed an antibacterial body wash and antimicrobial cream to apply inside their nostrils. Soon they were given the all clear and could resume their duties.

That was in 2012 and since then, no one else at Addenbrooke's has tested positive for that MRSA strain again. "Not only did genome sequencing demonstrate an outbreak more effectively than standard infection control, it identified a carrier," says Sharon Peacock of the University of Cambridge, another member of the team. "It was actionable information. If you can detect it early you can nip it in the bud and prevent further infections."

Deadly pneumonia

Other groups are starting to use bacterial genome sequencing too. Around the same time as the Addenbrooke's investigation, a similar approach was being used to stop a deadly outbreak of antibiotic-resistant pneumonia at a hospital in Bethesda, Maryland, which killed 11 people.

The technique is also being used to investigate the emergence of new pathogens from animals. It has shown, for instance, that Danish farmers infected with a new form of MRSA were catching it from their sheep. "The advantage is that you can identify the bacteria or virus down to the individual," says Mark Holmes at the University of Cambridge, who led that research. "It's the fine detail." It may even be able to help clarify whether badgers in the UK really are a major source of tuberculosis infection in cattle.

Genome sequencing is unlikely to replace shoe-leather epidemiology as a way of investigating novel disease outbreaks, but it will increasingly be applied alongside it. The technique might even help predict the emergence of dangerous new pathogens before they start killing people. "Should we be scanning for outbreaks by sequencing water from a sewage plant?" Pybus wonders. "You've got the viral population of a city being excreted into waste water."

That's something for public health doctors to consider in future. In the meantime, microbes continue their silent evolution within our bodies, biding their time until the opportunity to jump to another person presents itself. Inevitably it will, triggering another outbreak of disease.

This time, though, the germ detectives will be waiting for them. ■

"Alarm bells rang when another baby tested positive for MRSA, changing the study into a live investigation"

CHAPTER TWO

FIGHTING INFECTION

Every last trace

How do you wipe a disease off the face of a planet, asks Meera Senthilingam

O N 12 October 1977, Ali Maow Maalin, a 23-year-old hospital cook in the city of Merca, Somalia, embarked on a journey that would both change his life and mark a moment in history. He encountered a driver in need of directions, and ended up joining him and his passengers to help guide them to their destination, just 15 minutes away.

The passengers were two children. He saw they had rashes and bumps on their face but thought nothing of it. Had he realised the

nature of the place he was directing them to, he might have thought twice. A few months earlier there had been an outbreak of smallpox in a nomadic community north of Merca, and health officials were sending suspected carriers to an isolation camp in the hope of stamping out the disease.

That is where Ali was now headed. Afraid of needles, he had never been vaccinated against smallpox. Ali's 15 minutes of kindness was enough to leave him infected with it – although

After surviving smallpox, Ali Maalin joined the campaign to rid his country of polio

smallpox remain a solo success?

This question has become especially pressing in recent years. Polio was declared a target for eradication in 1988, and health workers had seemed on course to meet their deadline of stamping it out by 2018. But in May 2014, the World Health Organization (WHO) declared polio a public health emergency of international concern. At the start of 2014, polio was endemic in just three countries – Pakistan, Afghanistan and Nigeria – meaning the virus was circulating in their populations without being introduced from outside. However, the recent upheavals in Syria and Iraq led to a surge in polio cases in 2013, with cases also cropping up in Ethiopia, Somalia, Equatorial Guinea and Cameroon.

Smallpox proved that it was possible to eradicate a disease. Why is polio proving so tricky? And might some of the other scourges of our time, from malaria to measles, perhaps even HIV, one day be similarly squashed?

"When smallpox succeeded, there were masses of people saying this disease and that disease could be eradicated – it became ridiculous," says Donald Hopkins, who directs health programmes at the non-profit Carter Center in Atlanta, Georgia. The reality is that although many diseases have been discussed as potential targets for eradication, only three have ever been formally targeted on a global scale: malaria, dracunculiasis (also called guinea-worm disease) and polio. Malaria was set as a target for eradication four years before smallpox, but early setbacks such as insecticide resistance stalled progress. Its eradication could soon be back on the table, but until then, efforts against dracunculiasis and polio are all we have at this level.

Even these two campaigns are starting to lag. "Smallpox was quick once decided," says Dina Pfeifer, programme manager for vaccine-preventable diseases and immunisation at the WHO. "We are suffering fatigue today because some efforts are taking a long time."

When the campaign to eradicate dracunculiasis was launched, it seemed a relatively easy target: the parasitic guinea worm was confined to limited regions of Asia and Africa, and simply supplying clean drinking water could, in theory, wipe it out.

People who drink water contaminated with the parasite's larvae develop a painful blister on their lower leg or foot about a year later. They often try to relieve the pain by dipping their leg in water, which induces the mature female, lurking in the blister, to burst out and release her larvae. "It's a disease that no textbook can prepare you for," says Hopkins.

He has been running the WHO's eradication campaign since 1986, and was heavily involved in the fight against smallpox before that.

In 1980, at the outset of the dracunculiasis campaign, there were 3.5 million cases of the disease in 21 countries. In 2013, there were just 148 cases reported – in Chad, Mali, Ethiopia and South Sudan. "Theoretically, it could be gone by 2015," said Hopkins at the time. He claims to be immune to pessimism – an important trait when fighting a tenacious disease. The total for 2014 was 126 cases.

Million dollar search

Often the closer we are to wiping out a disease, the harder it gets. Public health teams can't easily access the remote rural areas harbouring the last pockets of guinea-worm infection, assuming they even know where these are. When they do reach them, they may have just one or two cases to deal with, making it a very expensive enterprise for scant returns. "A million dollar search in Guinea found only one case," says Sandy Cairncross at the London School of Hygiene and Tropical Medicine, who helped fight the disease in West Africa in the 1990s. Even some at the Carter Center are alarmed at the costs, but it is important to continue the fight, Hopkins insists. "If you leave it now, it will come back and spread."

This is the danger with polio. A war zone, as large parts of Iraq and Syria have become, is the perfect setting for such an infectious disease to flourish. Here though, a regional vaccination drive has been very successful, with just one case in 2014 reported in Syria and two in Iraq. In the case of polio, 80 per ❯

unlike millions before him, he recovered. His was the last ever naturally occurring case of smallpox.

Smallpox remains the only human disease to have been deliberately eradicated from the face of the Earth. Defined as the complete and permanent reduction of a disease to zero new cases at a global level, eradication is a challenge to say the least. Even more impressive is the speed with which it was achieved. In 1967, smallpox was responsible for 1.5 million deaths; 10 years later it was gone – although the official declaration came in 1980.

Health benefits aside, there were also sound economic reasons for wiping out the disease. Treating and vaccinating against smallpox, and its impact on the economic productivity of the people who contracted it, cost the world an estimated $1.5 billion each year in the mid-1970s, yet the total cost of the eradication programme was just $300 million. So, more than 35 years on, why does

POLIO
1988 - 345,000 cases
2014 - 359 cases

GUINEA WORM
1986 - 3.5 million cases
2014 - 126 cases

SMALLPOX
1967 - 131,697 cases
2014 - Eradicated

Polio on the way out

Even with effective strategies and government commitment, stamping out the final cases of polio is tricky

Total cases **(thousand)**

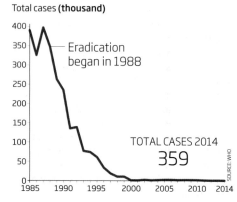

- Eradication began in 1988

TOTAL CASES 2014
359

cent of the population needs to be vaccinated in order to achieve herd immunity: a state in which it becomes difficult for the virus to spread.

Polio vaccination is more challenging in Nigeria and Pakistan. In both countries, conspiracy theories revolving around sterilisation or poisoning by the vaccine have made people suspicious of those delivering the injections, some of whom have been shot at. Educating people about the benefits of vaccination then becomes crucial.

In the case of Somalia, Maalin joined the campaign to rid his country of polio. He was able to use his own experience of smallpox as an object lesson in why vaccination was necessary, even convincing some militia leaders it was safe. But it was a case of two steps forward, one step back. After being declared polio-free in 2008, the country reported 194 cases in 2013. Reduced vaccine coverage and then a single infected person arriving from abroad are thought to have sparked the outbreak. Immunisation efforts look to be paying off now, though, with just five cases reported in 2014.

Like smallpox, polio is a viral disease with an effective vaccine that, properly used, can provide lifelong immunity. So why hasn't polio been eradicated in the same way?

Military measures

Hopkins became involved in the smallpox campaign straight out of medical school. He believes it worked because it had two key things on its side: a potent vaccine and the support of governments across the globe – most of which had first-hand experience of grappling with the disease.

But times have changed since the final pockets of smallpox were dealt with. "For smallpox they used very military measures, putting people in quarantine with armed soldiers around them," says Peter Piot, director of the London School of Hygiene and Tropical Medicine. "I'm not sure that would work today."

So to deal with the final pockets of polio, the strategy remains one of trying to vaccinate as many people as possible. "You think you're close to the end and then you find a new outbreak," says Pfeifer. "We need to target all immunity gaps to stop transmission."

For some diseases, eradication may simply be too tough a goal to achieve. But that doesn't mean their incidence can't be reduced to near zero, at least in some areas – a strategy known as elimination (see "A world without HIV?",

OLIVIER ASSELIN

right). And elimination can itself pave the way for eradication, by proving to governments and funders that it is possible to rid entire areas of a disease.

Measles is one disease being targeted for global elimination by 2020, though with large outbreaks in Europe, central Asia and California in 2014 and 2015, that target is looking hard to reach. Once again, an effective vaccine exists, although 95 per cent of the population needs to receive it in order to stop the virus from spreading. That's a far higher proportion than with any other disease. On the other hand, measles is easy to diagnose: it only infects humans, and once vaccinated, you're immune for life.

So why are we not being more ambitious? "It is biologically feasible to eradicate measles," says Peter Strebel from the expanded programme on immunisation at the WHO. Measles has already been eliminated in the Americas, with the last endemic case in 2002; any cases since then have been the result of people arriving from abroad. But as long as measles exists elsewhere "there is always a risk of importation", says Strebel, especially with today's level of global travel. It is also difficult to run several eradication programmes in parallel. With efforts against polio still ongoing, now is not the time to be setting a date for measles eradication, Strebel says.

Global elimination of measles would in itself be a massive achievement. One definition of elimination is slashing the incidence of a disease until it is no longer a

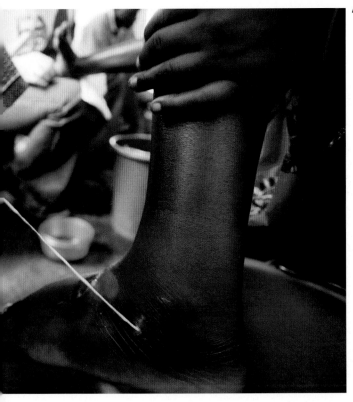

"It is biologically feasible to eradicate measles. But it is difficult to run several eradication programmes in parallel"

Clean drinking water could see off guinea-worm disease (left). For polio, the strategy is vaccination

public health burden. In theory, this should protect those pockets of the population who remain unvaccinated.

What about malaria? Is there any hope of eliminating it over time, or even wiping it off the face of the Earth? The original campaign to eradicate malaria was launched in 1955, although the US had begun its own campaign to stamp out the disease nine years earlier. It seemed to be working; by 1951, the disease had been eliminated from all 50 states.

Similar successes were seen in Europe.

Yet these efforts, which mainly relied on the use of insecticides, failed when attempted globally. Even small gaps in insecticide coverage enabled mosquitoes carrying the malaria parasite to survive and re-establish themselves. The plug was finally pulled on the project in 1968.

When aiming to remove a disease completely, a vaccine is a massive bonus. "You need a simple intervention, and a vaccine

is still our best bet," explains Piot. "When there is heavy transmission, even an imperfect vaccine can make a difference."

The recent success of malaria vaccines in clinical trials has brought some hope. For example, the RTS,S vaccine builds up antibodies that block malaria parasites from gaining a foothold in the body. Although only partially effective, its arrival, combined with other strategies such as bed nets and mosquito control, has put talk of malaria eradication – or at the very least, elimination – back on the table.

In 2007, the African Union launched the African Malaria Elimination Campaign, with the aim of reducing infections to zero in countries with low rates, such as Botswana – as well as reducing deaths and illness by 75 per cent in countries where the disease is more common. The strategy involves intensifying measures such as the distribution of insecticide-treated bed nets and, as with all disease control, requires continuous political support.

Back to Somalia and Ali Maalin, who fought against polio quite literally to his death. In July 2013, Maalin was out on a polio vaccination campaign in Somalia, during its surge in reinfections, when he fell ill and died – reportedly of malaria. In his life, he witnessed the eradication of one disease and the near-eradication of two others. Perhaps the rest of us will live long enough to see these – and perhaps other diseases – similarly obliterated. ∎

A WORLD WITHOUT HIV?

The development of antiretroviral drugs against HIV has transformed the prospects of people infected with the virus. But can we ever turn the clock back to a world without HIV? The lack of an effective vaccine against the virus makes eradication unfeasible, at least for now. But some argue that elimination - bringing infection rates to near zero in some areas - could be a reasonable goal.

Conventional practice has been to prescribe antiretrovirals only when an infected person's white blood cell count falls below a certain level. But a clinical trial in 2011 found that giving these drugs from the moment people tested positive for HIV dramatically reduced their viral levels - and so slashed transmission to their partners by 96 per cent. Jan Hontelez from Erasmus MC

in Rotterdam, the Netherlands, has since modelled how such early treatment might impact the prevalence of HIV in South Africa, which has one of the highest infection rates in the world. His results suggest that if it were adopted across the country, "we reach elimination, optimistically, in 17 years". Even the conventional use of antiretroviral drugs might lead to elimination within 27 years if everyone who needed the drugs received them," his models suggest.

However, these make a lot of assumptions, not least that large numbers of people would volunteer for HIV testing and that they'd all take their drugs according to the prescribed regime. "I'm not as optimistic as the modellers. Life is different," says Peter Piot, director of the London School of Hygiene and Tropical Medicine.

Re-educating superbugs could save lives, as **Clare Wilson** discovers

JAMIE GRILL/GETTY

IT IS a superbug with quite a few tricks up its sleeve. Found pretty much everywhere, from soil and water to your skin and lungs, it thrives with oxygen and without. It can dine on diesel and tar. It is naturally resistant to many antibiotics and can rapidly evolve resistance to all the rest. And for its party piece, it can stand upright and walk. Step forward *Pseudomonas aeruginosa*.

What makes *Pseudomonas* and many other kinds of bacteria so deadly, though, is their ability to work together. Millions of them can join forces to form powerful armies that overwhelm our defences.

It is not surprising, then, that if you are ever unlucky enough to end up in intensive care, there is a chance *Pseudomonas* will kill you. In fact, the real mystery has been why it doesn't kill more of us. Even though the bacterium infects just about everyone who remains on a ventilator for a long period, only 15 per cent ever get pneumonia.

Now we may have discovered why. It turns out that the armies of *Pseudomonas* are often greatly weakened by indiscipline in the ranks. They come to be dominated by cheaters and layabouts, which feast on the spoils of victory but ignore all orders to attack. These selfish bacteria multiply faster than the obedient ones, resulting in a less aggressive infection.

This discovery opens up the possibility of a radical new way to tackle superbug infections: deliberately encouraging the growth of cheater strains, perhaps by injecting them into people. Some think it is a crazy and dangerous idea. For others it is a bold approach that is sorely needed as antibiotic resistance grows (see "Going to extremes", page 46).

Long seen as simple, solitary creatures, in the past few decades we have come to understand that bacteria are actually highly social. Large groups of bacteria can cooperate closely – and it is this ability to work together that makes some species so dangerous to us.

Many disease-causing bacteria have dual personalities. In small numbers they live independently and peaceably within us, staying beneath the immune system's radar. On reaching a critical mass, however, they turn nasty or virulent, and start to behave like an army. Sometimes these armies build fortifications, cementing their bodies together to form tough biofilms. Or they may march together in vast swarms and launch an all-out attack. Now they get noticed, but their sheer force of numbers can overwhelm the immune system.

Don't cooperate

These discoveries made researchers realise that it might not be necessary to kill bacteria to prevent them harming us. Instead, we could just stop them ganging up on us.

The most obvious way to do this is to stop them talking to each other. Bacteria gauge their population size through a system called quorum sensing. They continuously pump out a chemical signal; if only a few individuals are around, its level remains low, but in a crowd the chemical gets more concentrated. When the bacteria detect that numbers are on their side, they turn virulent.

Several groups have been trying to develop drugs that block these signals. Unfortunately, progress on such "quorum quenchers" has been slow, with compounds that work well in the Petri dish failing in tests on animals. Having other ways of subverting bacterial cooperation wouldn't hurt.

That's where the cheater bacteria come in. Their significance was discovered not by microbiologists but by sociobiologists, who

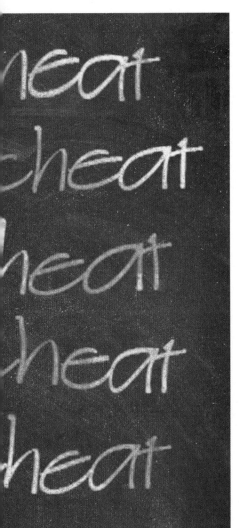

Only a few bacteria actually get to form spores, though – around nine out of 10 sacrifice themselves in the process of producing the fruiting body. In 2000, it was shown that some mutant strains cheat by always trying to form spores rather than sacrificing themselves. When these cheaters take over a population, they can destroy its ability to form fruiting bodies, sometimes even leading to extinction.

Does the pattern hold for disease-causing bacteria? When they attack en masse, bacteria start pumping out toxins and other chemicals. These "virulence factors" take a lot of energy to manufacture, so cheaters would reap the benefits of these compounds without paying the price of making them.

The first evidence of this in *Pseudomonas* related to iron scavenging. Bacterial growth is often limited by a lack of iron, so when

Hospitals in Switzerland. Van Delden has long battled *Pseudomonas* in his intensive care units. The bacteria colonise the breathing tube of anyone who has one in place for long enough, and some people develop pneumonia as a result.

The infection is hard to fight as resistance develops to whatever antibiotics are used, and the patients are too sick to cope with the drugs' side effects. "The first time you can treat with not too many problems, the second episode will be more difficult and the third will be a nightmare," says van Delden.

What has long baffled doctors is why *Pseudomonas* infection causes pneumonia in only 10 to 15 per cent of people on ventilators. "There are no risk factors that clinicians could identify on the patient's side," says van Delden. "This suggests the bacteria are different."

As more and more papers were published

> "What makes bacteria so deadly is their ability to join forces to form powerful armies that overwhelm our defences"

study the evolution of societies and of traits such as altruism and spite. In the animal kingdom, whenever some individuals cooperate for the greater good, others evolve to take advantage. In other words, some animals benefit from the community's hard work without doing anything themselves, which can sometimes lead to the community's downfall.

Sociobiologists suspected the same must be true of bacteria – and they were right. The first cheaters were spotted in populations of a soil-dwelling microbe called *Myxococcus xanthus*. When food runs low, thousands of individuals behave as if they are a multicellular organism, clustering together to form tiny towers, called fruiting bodies, that release spores.

Pseudomonas turn virulent, they usually release a virulence factor called pyoverdin, which scavenges iron from human proteins. Some mutants had been discovered, however, that don't produce pyoverdin. Looking at it from an evolutionary perspective, sociobiologists realised that these mutants thrived because they were cheaters: why go to the trouble of making a costly molecule like pyoverdin if you can hang around and steal iron freed by the pyoverdin made by others?

Other strains are even bigger cheaters – they have mutations in a master switch that controls production of many virulence factors, and so can coast along doing very little work. In 2007, two groups published work around the same time showing that if these strains are introduced into a colony of normal *Pseudomonas* bacteria growing in a test tube, the mutants take over.

"These mutants had been found naturally and nobody really knew why," says Steve Diggle, a microbiologist at the University of Nottingham in the UK, who led one of the groups. His team's work proved that not spending precious energy making virulence factors gives the cheaters a big competitive advantage. "That raises the question of, can you use this?"

Yes, says Christian van Delden, an infectious disease specialist at Geneva University

on bacterial cheating, van Delden began to suspect that this could be the explanation. Perhaps people who didn't develop pneumonia had *Pseudomonas* infections weakened by cheaters.

The chance to test this idea arose when van Delden was involved in a trial of an existing antibiotic called azithromycin. Though it is poor at killing *Pseudomonas* in the Petri dish, van Delden's team had found the drug somehow blocks its quorum-sensing systems. A Swiss biotech firm called Ambix applied for a new patent on the antibiotic based on its quorum-quenching activity, and asked van Delden to test it on people on ventilators. To show the drug was working through quorum quenching, repeated sputum samples were taken and the bacteria analysed to see if they had responded to quorum-sensing signals and turned virulent.

The trial ended abruptly when Ambix's US patent application was rejected, but van Delden realised he could still make use of the data. He teamed up with Angus Buckling, an evolutionary biologist now at the University of Exeter, UK, who had done some of the early work on *Pseudomonas* cheating. "It was a fantastic opportunity," says Buckling.

Sure enough, their team found that more than half of people infected with non-cheater bacteria got pneumonia, ❯

The mystery is why
superbug infections
don't kill more people

NYCSHOOTER/GETTY

"The armies are weakened by cheaters
and layabouts, which feast on the spoils
of victory but ignore all orders to attack"

compared with less than a tenth of those infected with cheater strains.

Studies like this could one day change the treatment people receive in intensive care. Because *Pseudomonas* evolves resistance so easily, at the moment doctors wait until people show signs of pneumonia before giving them antibiotics. But if they could identify the 15 per cent of people likely to get pneumonia, they could treat them earlier, potentially saving lives.

A more radical approach would be to inoculate the vulnerable 15 per cent with a dose of cheater bacteria. In theory they would outcompete the virulent bacteria and stop the infection progressing. But it would be risky. "Who is going to sanction introducing a pathogen?" says Buckling. "All it's going to take is one case going wrong."

Instead van Delden's group is exploring

ways to encourage the spontaneous evolution of cheating. One way to do this is to stop cheaters being punished.

When *Pseudomonas* turn virulent, among the toxins they produce may be pyocins that kill other bacteria. At the same time, they start producing pyocin-blocking compounds to avoid shooting themselves in the foot. Cheaters that ignore the signal to turn virulent, however, do not ready their defences, and thus are killed along with unrelated bacteria. So if we could find drugs that block pyocins, they should help cheating mutants to survive and take over populations, rendering the infection harmless.

Diggle's group in Nottingham, meanwhile, is exploring the radical approach. In 2009 his team deliberately infected the wounds of mice with various strains of *Pseudomonas*. They found that those infected with cheater strains

were twice as likely to survive as those infected with normal bacteria. Mice dosed with a 50-50 mix of cheaters and normal bacteria were also twice as likely to survive, which suggests giving cheaters to people already infected with normal strains might help save lives.

Diggle hopes this daring strategy might work in people with severe *Pseudomonas* infections in burns. "I don't think it's as crazy as it seems," he says. "It's very early days and there are huge regulatory hurdles to overcome, but there's potential for it to work."

If it fulfils its promise, the approach could help treat many kinds of infections. In 2008, Richard Novick, a microbiologist at New York University, showed that cheats that ignore quorum-sensing signals exist among *Staphylococcus aureus*, another common cause of wound infections and pneumonia, especially in hospital patients. That's big news because the spread of *S. aureus* resistant to the antibiotic methicillin, better known as MRSA, is a huge problem. In a study published in 2012, Novick's colleague Bo Shopsin found that in people with pneumonia caused by *S. aureus*, the presence of cheaters made the people more likely to survive.

Whether any of the strategies to exploit bacterial cheating will bear fruit remains to be seen. But these discoveries are changing the way researchers think. At first, mainstream microbiologists were doubtful about applying theories about social evolution to bacteria. "They are interested in the 'how' questions, we are interested in the 'why'," says Diggle. "It was received with a bit of scepticism."

Combining these approaches is leading to a wealth of new insights. For instance, Sarah Reece, a parasitologist at the University of Edinburgh, UK, has found that the organism that causes malaria alters its reproductive strategy depending on how many of its fellows are present in the same human and how closely related they are. "This could be a new opportunity to control these creatures," says Reece.

It is even relevant to industry. Cheating among *Lactococcus lactis* has been found to explain why some batches of cheese fail to ferment properly.

It's one thing to inject bacteria into a Stilton, quite another to stick them into a person. Yet it is no exaggeration to say that the rise of antibiotic resistance is one of the biggest threats to our health. If a time comes when people are dying because conventional antibiotics are no longer any use, injecting them with "cheatobiotics" instead might look a lot less crazy. ■

The mark of noro

The audacious norovirus spreads so readily that millions are sickened every year, yet its inner workings still elude us. **Dan Jones** investigates

T HAS almost certainly happened to you. You suddenly start feeling very ill and rush to the bathroom. Soon you don't know which way to turn as you alternate between projectile vomiting and diarrhoea. And if that were not enough, your head throbs, your muscles ache and your stomach hurts.

We tend not to take norovirus too seriously because the misery doesn't last long. The vast majority of people recover after a day or two. But outbreaks can affect so many people at once – particularly in confined environments like childcare centres, barracks, hospitals and cruise ships – that they cause a lot of disruption. It is common for wards to have to be closed and even schools shut.

What's more, it affects a huge number of people each year. Norovirus made headlines in the UK at the end of 2012 when a million people caught it in just a couple of months. Yet such numbers are not unusual. In the US, norovirus infects 20 million people a year, at an estimated annual cost of $8 billion in lost productivity and healthcare bills.

For the very young and very old, or people with weakened immune systems, the disease can cause more than misery. It hospitalises 70,000 people each year in the US and kills about 800. At least 200,000 people die of it in poorer countries, mostly children under 5.

> "A single batch of vomit contains enough viruses to infect 3 million people"

Yet there are no treatments or vaccines for norovirus. So do we just have to put up with this nauseating infection, or is there something we can do?

There are reasons why norovirus runs rampant; it is a pretty amazing virus. It may be the perfect human pathogen, says Aron Hall, an epidemiologist at the Centers for Disease Control and Prevention in Atlanta, Georgia. For starters, it is highly infectious. Exposure to as few as 18 virus particles can lead to infection, compared with upwards of 1000 for flu. Infected people produce billions of viruses, which are shed in vomit and faeces.

As a result, even with strict hygiene it is difficult to stop the virus spreading. It can strike at any time, but outbreaks are most common in the winter months as people ➤

"About a fifth of people have genetic protection against norovirus and almost never get infected"

spend more time with each other in enclosed spaces. Most infections are thought to be from person to person, either as a result of direct contact or by touching contaminated surfaces. Such contamination is hard to get rid of as the virus is very tough: it can withstand many chemical detergents, heat up to 60 °C, freezing, and it survives on surfaces like doorknobs and tablecloths for as long as two weeks. In pooled groundwater, it may survive for months or even years.

Another major source of infection is food. A single sick food-handler at a restaurant or factory can infect hundreds of people, while shellfish such as mussels become infectious if grown in waters contaminated with sewage. The danger is greatest with uncooked foods, such as salads and oysters.

The virus can even spread aerially: when vomit splashes on a hard surface, billions of viruses fly into the surrounding air and can be inhaled or swallowed. In theory, one batch of vomit could contain enough viruses to infect 3 million people.

A 2009 study of an outbreak at a scouting jamboree in the Netherlands estimated that each person who fell sick infected 14 others on average. If this is typical, it would make norovirus one of the most contagious diseases on the planet.

Another extraordinary thing about norovirus infections is that people vary immensely in their susceptibility. With most viruses, such as measles or chickenpox, people develop lifelong immunity after catching the disease or being vaccinated. Some viruses,

like colds and flus, mutate so fast that people can catch the diseases again every few years despite still being immune to the older strains.

Yet about a fifth of people almost never get infected by noroviruses. The virus is thought to get into cells by binding to carbohydrates called histo-blood group antigens. These coat the surface of mucosal cells, such as those lining our airways and intestines. Different strains target different HBGAs, but a particular sugar group seems to be important. People without a working copy of the *FUT2* gene do not produce this sugar, and a 2003 study led by Ralph Baric, a virologist at the University of North Carolina at Chapel Hill, showed that they are not infected by common norovirus strains even if exposed to high doses. Later work has shown that these people are vulnerable to a few strains, however.

Another tenth of the population lack this genetic protection but can usually fight off the virus before it takes hold, says Baric. "These people have most likely developed long-term immune protection after a previous infection." In other words, they respond in the way you would expect. But even then, having long-term protection against one strain of norovirus does not necessarily protect against other strains, and there are plenty of them.

So far about 40 strains have been identified. The viruses that infect humans usually belong to one of two main groups, called genogroups GI and GII. Within each genogroup there are lots of variants, or genotypes, designated GI.1, GI.2 and so on.

Not only are there lots of different strains,

in the majority of people the immunity gained by fighting off an infection does not seem to last long. Small studies in which people were deliberately exposed to the virus suggest that most people can be reinfected by the same strain after as little as six months. Why this is so remains a mystery.

Immune hijacker

Amazingly, we do not even know exactly which gut cells the virus infects. Studies of tissue taken from the intestines of infected people have failed to reveal its presence, and so far all attempts to infect human cells growing in culture have failed. This makes studying norovirus extremely difficult because it cannot be grown in the lab.

In fact, much of what we think we know actually comes from studying related viruses. In 2004, researchers managed to grow a mouse strain of norovirus in cells in culture. They found that it infected two kinds of immune cells, including dendritic cells. Found in the lining of the gut, these cells usually act as immune sentinels, alerting the rest of the immune system to whatever's in the gut. But norovirus seem to be able to hijack them.

Another thing that is not clear is whether norovirus is becoming more common. Some researchers think it might be, due to factors such as our rising consumption of prepared foods and an increase in norovirus breeding grounds in the form of care homes and cruise ships. But we do not have any reliable long-term records. Most people who fall ill never go to the doctor, let alone have any samples taken for testing, so researchers can only guess at the true number of cases. A 2012 study found that even in hospitals, half of all cases may go undiagnosed, because not everyone has the full set of symptoms.

It does seem likely that there was a sudden jump in norovirus outbreaks in the 1990s, because this is when pandemic variants of the GII.4 strain emerged. This strain had been around since at least 1967, but in 1996 a variant emerged that rapidly spread around the world infecting unprecedented numbers of people. This soon became a pattern: it happened again in 2002, 2004, 2006, 2009 and 2012.

Studies led by Peter White at the University of New South Wales in Sydney, Australia, suggest that GII.4 has become the dominant form of the virus because it evolves more rapidly than other strains. Like all RNA viruses, noroviruses mutate fast, but GII.4 viruses have an especially high mutation rate because the enzyme that copies their RNA is

Winters of discontent

Norovirus cases soar in winter. The disease struck early in 2012 in the UK, raising fears of a severe outbreak, but in the end the overall number of cases was no higher than normal

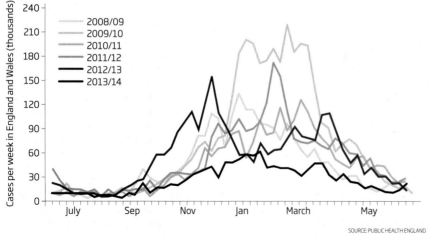

SOURCE: PUBLIC HEALTH ENGLAND

It takes as few as 20 virus particles to infect you and cause gastroenteritis

HOW TO DODGE NORO

What can be done to avoid two days hunched over, or sat on, a toilet? The first and most obvious thing, says John Harris of Public Health England, is to keep your hands clean by washing with old-fashioned soap and running water. The evaporating alcohol gels found in hospital dispensers do a good job of killing bacteria, but they are not as effective against norovirus. After the gel has evaporated, many live viruses will be still left on your hands, he says.

If you do come down with norovirus, stay at home for three days after your symptoms have subsided, especially if you handle food or work in healthcare. Don't try to please your boss by rushing back to the office as soon as you go a day without vomiting or diarrhoea: you will still be shedding billions of virus particles, and are likely to infect legions of colleagues, friends and commuters. They will not thank you.

particularly error-prone. "It makes about one mistake every time the genome is copied," says White.

Unsurprisingly, the protruding parts of the virus – those our immune system learns to recognise – are evolving fastest. It appears that every few years, a new GII.4 emerges that is different enough to previous strains to evade what immunity still remains in the population, and this strain can then rampage around the world. So in some ways norovirus has become like flu, with new strains emerging regularly and sweeping across the world.

Yet there are key differences, too. One seems to be that although old flu strains tend to disappear, old strains of norovirus keep circulating at low levels. "From outbreak surveillance, we have seen that the seasonal winter peak really is mostly explained by outbreaks of the most common genotype, GII.4," says Marion Koopmans of the National Institute of Public Health in the Netherlands. "But if you take those outbreaks away, a much greater diversity of strains is seen."

The latest pandemic virus to emerge, called GII.4 Sydney, was first detected in Australia in March 2012. It became the dominant pandemic strain of the 2012/13 norovirus season, making headlines around the world. White's work suggests it formed when two GII.4 strains that had been circulating for a few years swapped parts of their genomes. "Someone got infected with those two viruses, which recombined to create GII.4 Sydney," he says.

In the UK, the seasonal uptick in norovirus cases typically seen in November began a month earlier in 2012. "We began seeing Sydney 2012 early, and more and more cases are attributable to this variant, although other GII.4 strains are also circulating," says David Allen, a virologist at Public Health England.

By January 2013, the strain was running wild in the US and Canada, too. Back in the UK, though, the number of cases fell much earlier than usual (see graph, left), and here at least the 2012/2013 season proved unexceptional in the end, though with a smaller, more unusual peak in April. "One thing that we've learned is that norovirus is unpredictable," says John Harris, an epidemiologist at Public Health England.

The capacity of norovirus to continually reinvent itself means that we will be living with pandemics for some time to come – unless, of course, a vaccine becomes available. A handful of candidates are currently being investigated. The furthest advanced is being developed by Takeda Vaccines in Bozeman, Montana. It consists of the main proteins that makes up the outer shell of the virus, which self-assemble into empty shells called virus-like particles that looks like the real deal to the immune system but cannot replicate themselves.

Vaccine hope

For its initial version, Takeda used GI shell proteins. The vaccine was sprayed into the noses of volunteers, who were later exposed to the GI.1 virus. Only 37 per cent developed gastroenteritis, compared with 69 per cent of those given a placebo.

"Although these results were promising, it left a lot of room for improvement," says Robert Atmar, an immunologist at Baylor College of Medicine in Houston, Texas, who led the trials. The company is now working on an injected version with both GI and GII proteins, which has now passed phase I trials.

Three other possible vaccines are being investigated at Arizona State University, the University of Cincinnati, and in a joint venture between the University of Tampere in Finland and Japanese firm UMN Pharma, but all are still at an early stage.

It remains to be seen whether these efforts will lead to a commercially viable vaccine. Even if a vaccine can be produced that provides strong protection against the strains included in it, it's far from clear how long the protection will last and whether it will work against different strains. New versions would have to be produced every few years to ensure it remains effective against the latest GII.4 strains, says Atmar.

Then again, a vaccine does not have to be 100 per cent effective. In theory at least, even a partially effective one could reduce the severity of people's symptoms, slow the virus's spread and reduce the overall number of cases. But at around £30 per dose, will individuals and healthcare providers regard it as a worthwhile investment?

It will be a few years before we find out. In the meantime, make like Lady Macbeth and wash your hands if you want to dodge this disgusting disease. ▪

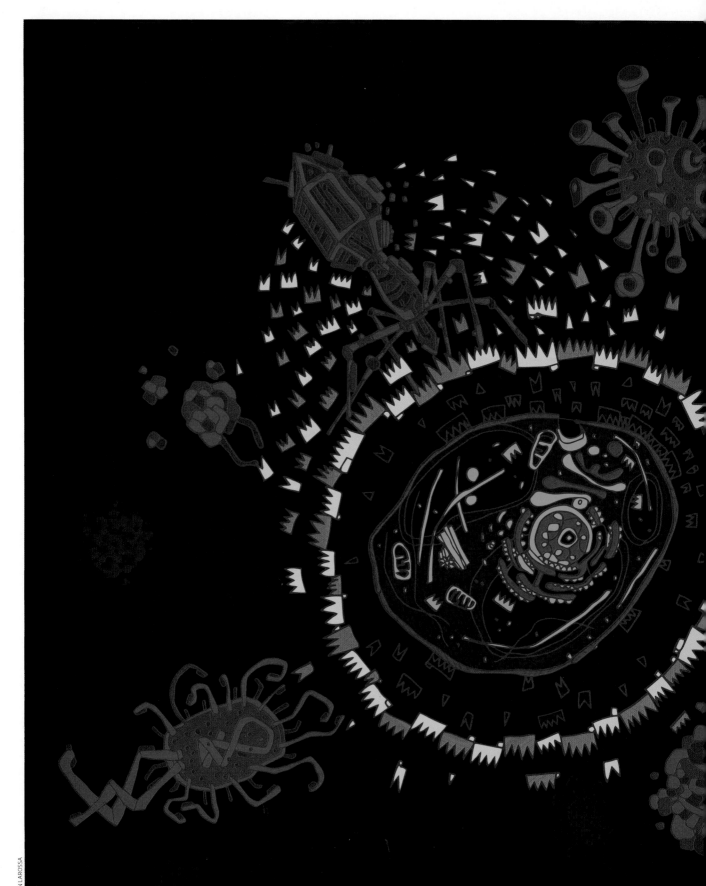

Small shot, big impact

Some vaccines seem to provide us with a host of extra benefits. **Michael Brooks** sees the cornerstone of modern medicine in a new light

HAVE a look at your left shoulder: if you are past your mid-twenties it almost certainly bears a circular scar. Do you remember how it got there? You queued up in the school hall, perhaps, or outside the nurse's office, watching your friends rubbing their arms as they walked away, relieved at having survived their BCG jab.

The Bacillus Calmette-Guérin vaccination was given to protect you from tuberculosis. What we are only just realising is that, in common with several other vaccines, it may have done far more than that.

There is growing evidence that vaccines have a wider-ranging influence on the immune system than we thought. In Africa, for instance, studies have shown that measles vaccine cuts deaths from all other infections combined by a third, mainly by protecting against pneumonia, sepsis and diarrhoea.

Even in the West, where it is far less common for children to die from infectious illnesses, there are still surprising benefits: some vaccines seem to reduce our susceptibility to eczema and asthma. Exactly what causes these "non-specific effects", as they are termed, is a mystery. But some scientists are arguing that, despite the uncertainties, it is time to start harnessing them more effectively.

In 2013, the World Health Organization, which is the main provider of vaccines in developing countries, asked a group of vaccine experts to investigate. "This could have huge implications for global healthcare," said committee member Christine Benn, a senior researcher at the Statens Serum Institute in Denmark. "Vaccines have been a fantastic success, but we can probably do much better by taking non-specific effects into account. An examination of these issues is long overdue."

Considering vaccines have been used since the 1800s and are the central plank of our public health system, it may seem hard to believe that such profound effects could have gone ignored all this time. In fact, an early 20th-century Swedish physician called Carl Näslund did notice something was up after the BCG vaccine was introduced in his country. Vaccinated children had a much higher chance of reaching their first birthday – even though TB normally kills older children.

In the 1940s and 50s, trials in the US and UK suggested that BCG-vaccinated children had a 25 per cent lower death rate from diseases other than TB. But no one took much notice until 30 years ago, when a Danish anthropologist called Peter Aaby began working in the West African state of Guinea-Bissau. In 1979 he witnessed a severe measles outbreak that killed 1 in 4 infants affected. Aaby arranged for measles vaccination to be introduced, but was surprised to see that even after the epidemic abated, immunised children were more likely to survive childhood. Aaby began digging, and discovered studies from elsewhere in Africa, as well as Bangladesh and Haiti, that also suggested measles vaccine gives a wider kind of protection. "We are collecting more and more data consistent with non-specific effects being very important," says Aaby.

What could the explanation be? Several lines of evidence suggest that our immune ➤

> "If past infections can alter the immune system, it is not a major leap to suggest that vaccines might also do so"

systems can be affected by many factors, including past encounters with microbes. Those microbes can be in the environment or a vaccine syringe. "If infections can alter the immunological milieu, it is not a major leap to suggest that vaccines might also do so," said Andrew Pollard, head of the Oxford Vaccine Group at the University of Oxford, in an editorial about Aaby's work in 2012.

According to the old view, vaccines work by priming what is known as our adaptive immune system. This consists of various defence cells circulating in the blood, which make antibodies and other molecules that recognise and latch on to specific foreign proteins on bacteria, viruses or other germs.

It is this lock-and-key specificity that is responsible for our immune memory. On our first encounter with the measles virus, say, the immune cells that make potent antibodies to it reproduce, giving rise to successive generations of daughter cells that make progressively more powerful antibodies. The end product is highly proficient measles-killing machines that linger in our bodies for years. That's why, if we re-encounter the virus, it is defeated so quickly we don't even notice.

But that may not be the whole story. Another, evolutionarily older, branch of our defences known as the innate immune system might also be playing a role. These cells are programmed to react to anything unfamiliar or untoward, such as the chemicals released when tissues are damaged, attacking any molecules or microorganisms that might pose a threat. In 2012, surprising evidence emerged that BCG stimulates the innate immune system as well as the adaptive one.

In people who received the shot, certain kinds of innate immune cells responded more strongly to bacterial and fungal pathogens completely unrelated to the TB bug. This is the first indication that the innate immune system reacts to vaccines, and the researchers suggested it could explain some of the general immune-boosting effects of BCG. "It's quite preliminary data, but it's very important," says Nigel Curtis, head of infectious diseases at the Royal Children's Hospital Melbourne and the University of Melbourne, Australia, who studies BCG.

The discovery may be only one part of the explanation for BCG's mysterious powers, though. For example, it emerged recently that memory cells of the adaptive immune system can target microbes they have not encountered before provided there is sufficient cross-reactivity with a bug the immune system has previously vanquished.

Tipping the balance

But the theory that probably has most evidence behind it concerns two competing arms of the adaptive immune system, known as type 1 and type 2 helper T-cells. Broadly, type 1 cells promote immune reactions against bacteria and viruses, while type 2 cells are geared towards fighting off parasitic worms in the gut. Both BCG and the measles vaccine seem to tip the balance to type 1, according to studies of the antibodies released into the bloodstream after vaccination.

Whatever the explanation is, we might be able to maximise the benefits, either by designing new vaccines or augmenting the effects of existing ones. But the WHO committee had another line of enquiry: there are suggestions that one vaccine could have harmful non-specific effects. The vaccine under suspicion is DTP, which prevents diphtheria, tetanus and pertussis, otherwise known as whooping cough.

It was Aaby, again, who first drew attention to this. These days, he is a vaccine researcher

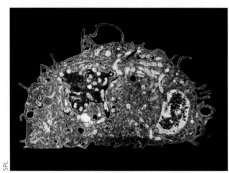

Our immune cells can see off TB bacteria (yellow), especially when primed by a vaccine

with the Statens Serum Institute, but is still based mainly in Guinea-Bissau. For several months in 2001 and 2002, health centres in the capital city, Bissau, ran out of DTP, and some infants never got their shot. Aaby noted that, among children who had been admitted to hospital for some reason, those who had had the shot were over twice as likely to die during their hospital stay. Further studies showed that the effect was particularly pronounced for girls.

No one knows why DTP might have such an effect. One possible explanation is that the pertussis component is made from killed whooping cough bacteria. There are other ways to make vaccines, including using live but weakened bacteria or viruses, with both BCG and the measles shot being this type. Killed vaccines, on the other hand, seem to tip the type 1/type 2 balance away from the bacteria and virus-fighting type 1 arm. Animal studies show that, for unknown reasons, females have a naturally stronger type 2 bias, which could explain the sex difference in mortality seen in Guinea-Bissau.

No one is suggesting we stop giving the DTP vaccine. The protection it provides is hugely beneficial – especially in the West. "Mortality from infectious diseases is incredibly low in wealthy countries in 2013," Pollard says. "Any non-specific effects are likely to be trivial and unmeasurable."

However, Aaby thinks that, in developing countries, there might be cleverer ways to schedule the vaccinations that increase their overall benefit. That's because BCG and measles seem to be such strong immune boosters they may be able to undo the immune-weakening effect of DTP. Aaby hopes to test giving DTP and BCG simultaneously, to see if it leads to an even more positive effect on the immune system overall. Another possibility is to shorten the time period between DTP and the next vaccination, by giving the measles vaccine earlier in life. "I'm in no doubt we could reduce mortality in low-income countries," Aaby says.

But the case for change is not yet strong enough. Most of Aaby's studies are what are known as "observational". That means they count the number of deaths in children who ended up getting different vaccines by chance. These kinds of studies can lead to bias in the results. "Randomised controlled trials are the only way you can answer this question," Pollard says.

"Aaby has written some papers, and some are more interesting and credible than others," says Paul Fine of the London School of Hygiene

A vaccine designed to protect against TB does more than we bargained for

While the primary aim is to see if BCG reduces allergic disease, a subset of 200 children will regularly have blood samples taken to see how the vaccine has affected their response to infectious diseases too. "That's a really interesting question," Pollard says.

There is no doubt that BCG has effects on the immune system that are wider than just defending against TB. It even stimulates an immune reaction against bladder cancer and is now a standard treatment for this disease, delivered directly into the bladder.

Despite the implications of his work, Aaby has had no end of trouble getting people to listen. That's probably because, even though most non-specific effects of vaccines are beneficial, the DTP effects are potentially harmful. And people are wary of triggering another scare like the one over the measles, mumps and rubella vaccine. "Our observations are clearly inconvenient," says Aaby.

That's a fair analysis, Pollard thinks. "The last thing to do is induce a loss of confidence in immunisation," he says. "What if children in poor countries die as a result?"

But Benn reckons it is important to be open about the unknowns. "People are scared of causing vaccination rates to drop overnight, but I think we could do with a more balanced discussion than there is now," she says.

Aaby is no troublemaker: he is a respected researcher leading networks of scientists. Support for non-specific effects of vaccines comes from dozens of studies involving many thousands of children. And vaccine researcher Richard Moxon at the University of Oxford has called Aaby's work "an important body of meticulously compiled data" that merits "serious consideration".

This is certainly a field with many unknowns: not only in the nature of non-specific effects, but also why they occur, and which other vaccines might cause them. Can we design new vaccines to maximise the benefits? While the mechanisms are not yet understood, says Calman MacLennan, a researcher for Novartis, any findings would certainly inform the design of future vaccines.

The WHO committee released its report in 2014. But while it acknowledged that non-specific effects were real, it concluded that the studies conducted so far are not sufficient to warrant any change in vaccination policy by the WHO and that more investigations, preferably randomised trials, are needed.

The questions cannot be answered soon enough for Curtis. "It needs investigating properly," he says. "If this is real, it's too important to ignore." ■

and Tropical Medicine, also a member of the WHO committee. "But we're not in a position where they should influence [vaccination] schedules."

Benn is not so sure. Although observational studies can be biased, any bias would tend to be towards showing DTP in a more favourable light, she says. That's because one reason for missing out on a vaccination is that you are already sick. So unvaccinated children are more likely to have higher death rates.

In addition, it is hard to get the go-ahead for randomised trials of vaccination schedules that are different to the WHO-recommended one. "Where randomised trials are just not possible, observational studies should definitely be taken into account," she says.

"We may be able to save several million more lives each year just by making better use of current vaccines," says Frank Shann of Melbourne's Royal Children's Hospital, who has worked on child health in the developing world for more than 30 years.

It is not just in poor countries that vaccine programmes may need to be reconsidered. Many developed countries are phasing out routine BCG vaccination as TB rates have receded. In the UK, for instance, BCG is now given only in certain inner city areas with large immigrant populations, who could have been infected in their home country.

Hygiene hypothesis

That might have affected more than our ability to fight off infectious diseases. Several studies have suggested BCG reduces eczema and asthma by 25 per cent, and reduces food allergies by 35 per cent. "That's not a small effect," Curtis points out.

The latest thinking is that allergies are caused by an imbalance in type 1 and 2 helper T-cells, with type 2 becoming too dominant. Allergies may be on the rise in the West because we no longer meet enough germs in childhood to strengthen the type 1 arm, according to the "hygiene hypothesis". If BCG does push the balance back to type 1, that could be why it reduces allergies.

Again, though, these studies were not purpose-built: they were done by looking back at data collected for other purposes and most were fairly small. In 2013, Curtis began a trial to investigate this issue in Melbourne, which will give the BCG shot to 1400 newborn children who wouldn't normally have got it.

Two answers to the looming antibiotic crisis are all around us – in great supply and free of charge. **Frank Swain** reports

A BREATH OF FRESH AIR

Light, airy hospital
rooms don't just have
psychological benefits

IT WAS a warm summer's night in 1968, at the height of the cold war. Two men stood on a lab roof at Porton Down, a UK ministry of defence site best known for its chemical and biological research programmes. On their minds was the grim prospect of biowarfare. If a bomb filled with deadly bacteria exploded above London, how long would the fallout remain dangerous?

To find out, microbiologists Henry Druett and K. R. May exposed microbes to air currents up on the roof. To stop the bacteria being blown away, the pair wound strands of spider silk around a comb, and gently dusted it with the common gut microbe, *Escherichia coli*.

In little over 2 hours, nearly all the bacteria trapped in these hand-crafted webs were dead. Yet when kept in boxes of rooftop air at identical temperature and humidity, over half the microbes were still viable after that time. What was going on? Something in fresh air was killing bacteria, only to vanish when the air was enclosed.

The researchers carried out many further experiments, showing that the strength of the mystery substance, dubbed the open air factor, varied from one night to the next. As the spectre of biowarfare receded, though, interest in their research fell away.

But could it be time to blow the dust off the old reports? The need for new weapons against infection has never been greater, with a growing number of pathogens developing resistance to the antibiotics we have been using against them. So researchers are turning to the infection control methods of an earlier age. "It's only now that patients are not getting better, because we're running out of antibiotics, that we're retracing our steps," says Stephanie Dancer, a microbiologist at NHS Lanarkshire in the UK, who is trying to revive interest in these strategies.

The Porton Down researchers were not the first to notice the medical benefits of fresh air. In the mid-19th century, British soldiers in the Crimean war were less likely to die on the battlefield than from diseases they caught in the dirty field hospitals. Pioneering nurse Florence Nightingale famously slashed hospital death rates with a host of improvements – including throwing open the windows. On her return home, she applied those lessons in British hospitals. "It is necessary to renew the air round a sick person frequently, to carry off morbid effluvia from the lungs and skin," she wrote.

Clinics built to her light, airy design became known as Nightingale wards: long, narrow rooms with sash windows reaching up to the ceiling that allowed fresh air to flow through. This arrangement not only diluted airborne pathogens but also actively killed them, according to the Porton Down research.

There was another crucial aspect of Nightingale wards: their long sides were south-facing to let in plentiful sunlight. Soon the health benefits of sunshine became more widely recognised, particularly for people with tuberculosis, which at the time caused around one in five deaths in crowded cities.

Sunlight not only kills airborne bacteria and those on the skin, but also seems to kill TB microbes in the body by boosting production of vitamin D, which has effects on the immune system. By the turn of the last century "solar clinics" were in vogue, utilising fresh air and sunlight as part of TB treatment. Hospital beds were wheeled on to balconies or conservatories with special glazing that allowed ultraviolet light to pass through.

Eventually UV lamps were developed for use within hospitals, but fell out of favour as the risks of skin cancer and cataracts became apparent. Today they are generally used only to sterilise surgical equipment.

Miracle in a dish

Everything in medicine changed in the years after Alexander Fleming famously discovered the dish of bacteria that had gone mouldy during his holiday. Compared with the almost miraculous powers of penicillin and other antibiotics, sunlight and fresh air seemed irrelevant.

By the 1960s many doctors thought that infectious diseases would soon be vanquished. "It was one new antibiotic after the other," says Dancer. "Open air factor was never going to kick-start major interest because when a patient got an infection, they got an antibiotic and they got better."

The notion that fresh air and sunshine are somehow good for us has lingered in the ❯

public consciousness, yet hospitals have turned away from Nightingale's principles, closing their windows and shutting out the sun. And once the oil crisis of the 1970s brought energy efficiency to the fore, open windows, which let precious heat escape, were phased out in favour of mechanical ventilation systems which recycle air and pass it through filters.

Today the need for energy efficiency is more pressing than ever, but hopes that infectious diseases might be conquered died long ago. New ones have been discovered at the rate of one every year for the past 30 years, and in the past decade we have faced down potential pandemics from SARS and bird flu.

What's more, diseases that were easily treatable in the 1960s are returning in antibiotic-resistant forms, including TB, pneumonia and gonorrhoea. Hospitals themselves are one of the biggest sources of antibiotic-resistant diarrhoea and wound infections. In the UK, some 9 per cent of hospital patients catch a new infection during their stay.

To make matters worse, there is a shortage of new antibiotics. Since 1990, the number of large firms trying to develop such drugs has dropped from 18 to four. England's chief medical officer Sally Davies focused on the

"US soldiers in the first Gulf war got more coughs and colds if they slept indoors than in tents"

problem in her 2013 report, warning that we face the prospect of diseases that were previously easy to control becoming much more significant threats to our health.

Although the pipeline of classic antibiotics is running dry (see "Going to extremes", page 46), there are various alternatives in the works. These include "quorum-blocking" drugs, which, rather than killing bacteria, merely stop them from mounting an attack (see "I must cheat", page 20). Such drugs should be less likely to trigger resistance than conventional antibiotics. Another option is phage therapies, using viruses genetically engineered to destroy bacteria.

These strategies are some years away from reaching the clinic, though, and it would be unwise to bank on their success. In the meantime, perhaps we can prepare for the looming post-antibiotic era by taking some lessons from the pre-antibiotic age. No one is

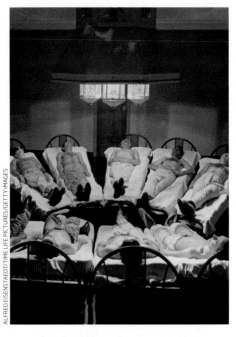

Before antibiotics, UV light was a standard therapy for tuberculosis

claiming that just drawing back the curtains and opening some windows can cure people who are already sick. But a few changes to hospital design could help prevent diseases spreading to those who are not yet infected.

After all, another old-fashioned disease prevention method is already paying dividends. Simply getting staff to wash their hands more is proving effective against the spread of superbugs MRSA and *Clostridium difficile* in the UK. MRSA rates in UK hospitals, for instance, have fallen by about 80 per cent since their peak in 2004. Hand-washing is not the only factor, but it seems an important one: the more alcohol hand rub a hospital uses, the lower its rates of MRSA.

Perhaps we would get similar benefits to infection control by resurrecting fresh air and sunshine, argues Dancer. "Hospitals of the future should be designed to allow windows to be opened and perhaps patients to be pushed outside in their beds," she says.

Dancer is not alone in her quest. A team from Imperial College London travelled to Lima, Peru, to see if traditional methods could reduce the spread of airborne TB, especially among people with HIV who are susceptible because of their weak immune systems. "The majority of TB transmission occurs where undiagnosed people mingle with susceptible ones," says epidemiologist Rod Escombe. "Crowded waiting rooms are a hotspot, as are outpatient clinics and emergency wards."

Lima has a mix of old-fashioned hospitals that rely on passive airflow, and modern ones with mechanical ventilation. By setting off carbon dioxide fire extinguishers within the hospitals and measuring how long it took for the gas to disperse, Escombe's team showed that ventilation rates in the old hospitals were more than double those of the

modern buildings.

As a result of that study, Lima's hospital managers are trying to add windows and skylights wherever possible. "Engineering a bit of a breeze is powerfully effective," says Carlton Evans, an infectious diseases researcher then at the city's Cayetano Heredia University, who took part in the work.

Sometimes extra skylights just aren't practical, though, so the team also investigated if a form of artificial sunlight might help. They installed a battery of old-

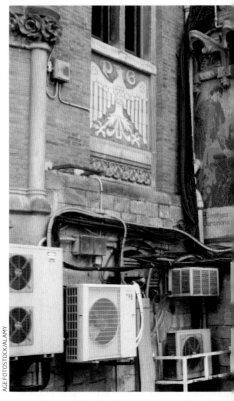

fashioned UV lamps in a TB ward, angled toward the ceiling so that the upper half of the room was bathed in light without exposing patients to the rays .

A standard test for airborne TB was used: keeping pens of guinea pigs in air from UV-treated and untreated wards. The lamps cut the number of animals that developed signs of TB infection from 35 to 10 per cent, suggesting patients would have been protected too.

This research has attracted interest from countries around the world – especially in places with high rates of TB and HIV. It has been repeated in South Africa, where the drier air seems to enhance the effect of UV even further. The lamps have been installed in hospitals in Peru, as well as Russia and Brazil. St Mary's Hospital in London also has one in the waiting room of its chest clinic. Stopping someone catching TB in the first place is always better than a long course of antibiotics. "We thought we had TB nailed," says Escombe. "The resurgence has reignited interest in ways to prevent transmission."

And there may be a way to make UV light safer so it can be used more widely in hospitals. UV is the portion of the spectrum with a wavelength of between 10 and 400 nanometres. At 207 nm, the UV is absorbed by protein molecules and therefore penetrates only a short way into human cells; it does not reach the DNA to cause mutations. Microbes,

Throwing open a few windows might be healthier than relying on ubiquitous air-conditioning

on the other hand, are so much smaller than human cells that they completely absorb the light and are killed (see diagram, right).

Now a lamp has been developed that emits only UV at 207 nm. Studies on cells grown in the lab have shown that this narrow band does not harm human skin tissue cultures yet kills bacteria, including MRSA.

The technology was originally designed for use during operations, to kill airborne bacteria that can settle in open wounds. "Bacteria are raining down on the wound during the entire surgery," says David Brenner, who led the research at Columbia University in New York. Brenner even reckons all hospital light bulbs could be augmented to emit UV at this desirable wavelength.

If we can artificially reproduce sunlight, could we perhaps do the same thing for the benefits of fresh air? Attempts have been made to spruce up stuffy hospital air with a form of the open air factor, discovered so long ago. The Porton Down team eventually concluded their mystery germ killer was hydroxyl radicals. These short-lived molecules are constantly produced in the atmosphere through reactions between ozone and water, catalysed by airborne organic chemicals from plants.

For a short while a UK firm called Inov8 was marketing a portable device to hospitals that produced a steady stream of hydroxyl radicals, using ozone, water and replaceable cartridges of an organic catalyst. The firm showed that hydroxyl radicals oxidise biological molecules and kill bacteria, yet are harmless to people. The device was found to reduce airborne bacteria in hospitals, but the firm went out of business in 2012.

Perhaps it would be simpler to throw open the windows? Not without considering the possible drawbacks, says George Sharples, a microbiologist at Liverpool John Moores University in the UK. In fact, UK hospital regulations state that windows within reach of patients must open no wider than 10 centimetres so that people cannot fall out.

Open-air regime

Draughts can also blow equipment around, and there may be more insidious dangers in the breeze. "Hospitals today aren't normally in remote areas – they're in city centres," Sharples says. Today's patients would be exposed to traffic pollutants, or if the clinic were near a rubbish dump, fungal spores, which pose a risk to newborns, the elderly and others with weak immune systems.

New hospitals do tend to be more spacious, and have fewer hospital-acquired infections, but no one is quite sure why. "Is it more space between patients, is it better airflow?" wonders Mark Wilcox, head of microbiology and pathology at Leeds Teaching Hospitals in

Sterilising rays

Ultraviolet light of the right wavelength can kill bacteria while leaving human cells unharmed

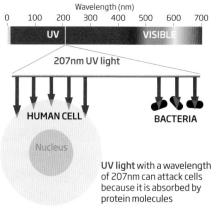

UV light with a wavelength of 207nm can attack cells because it is absorbed by protein molecules

Human cells are large enough that this UV light only penetrates the surface. Bacteria, on the other hand, are small and so are killed

the UK. "Or is it a better work environment for staff, leading to better compliance with infection prevention practice?"

The World Health Organization is not so reticent: in 2009 it published a report urging all healthcare settings to use natural ventilation as far as possible, even referencing Florence Nightingale. In Mumbai, India, an old-style sanatorium is being refitted as a clinic for people with drug-resistant TB, making use of an open-air regime. "It's well suited because of its high ceilings and open balconies," says Escombe. "We've come full circle in hospital design."

And it's not just hospitals where getting more fresh air circulating could reduce the spread of disease: there are benefits anywhere that people live closely together. For instance, US soldiers stationed in the Saudi Arabian desert during the first Gulf war got more coughs and colds if they slept in air-conditioned barracks than if they bedded down in tents and warehouses. Another study looking at Chinese college students found that 35 per cent of those who slept in poorly ventilated dorm rooms got an infection over the course of a year, compared with 5 per cent in rooms that were better ventilated.

In the future, we may well see architects, doctors and building managers working together to ensure that we live and work in environments that take account of our microbial companions. And in the meantime, perhaps we should take a leaf out of Nightingale's book, and whenever possible let a breath of fresh air into our homes. "The first canon of nursing, the first essential to the patient, is to keep the air he breathes as pure as the external air, without chilling him," she wrote. "Never be afraid of open windows." ▪

indiscriminately hitting all cells with very toxic molecules."

In theory, changing that should have been simple. Since Doxil's release, researchers have been developing techniques for decorating the capsules with antibodies that latch specifically on to tumours. But it has proved difficult to design a liposome envelope that is robust enough to prevent the active ingredient leaking out in transit, while also unloading its cargo quickly once the antibodies have docked. Too much of it is left inside by the time the body's defences discover the capsule and remove it, generally within a few days.

As so often on the tortuous routes of drug discovery, an alternative approach stretches back a long way. In the 1970s, researchers such as Robert Langer of the Massachusetts Institute of Technology began to develop controlled-release polymers for medical use. Unlike liposomes, which essentially contain a single ingredient, these polymers can be made from complex mixtures of molecules. By varying the recipe slightly, different drug-release properties can be induced.

Perhaps the most promising material is PLGA, a polymer that combines glycolic acid and lactic acid. Once inside the body, it slowly starts to break down. The more glycolic acid the mixture contains, the faster this happens, allowing drug makers to determine, to an extent, how soon the drug nestled within it is released. Implants using PLGA have been approved for human use since the mid-1990s,

inserted under the skin to release a steady trickle of the drug into the blood. Examples include the brain tumour treatment Gliadel and a prostate cancer implant called Zoladex.

In 2002, Langer teamed up with Omid Farokhzad of Harvard Medical School in Boston. The pair began to experiment with bringing together in one nanoscale package all the components needed for targeted, effective drug delivery: the controlled release core with the active ingredient inside, the surrounding PEG stealth cloak, and an outer layer of targeting antibodies. Such a package would be small enough to bring its cargo directly into cells. But this promise came with a problem. The large number of components and variables such as size, surface properties and rate of drug release and degradation made engineering the most effective drug a huge challenge.

To tackle it, Langer and Farokhzad have pioneered a way to generate an array of self-assembling candidates, using high-speed screening to pick out the best one. "To re-optimise the drug after encapsulation, you need to create libraries of nanoparticles with slightly different properties," says Farokhzad.

"Results so far seem to show the capsules' improved seek-and-destroy abilities: those treated are responding at half the dose of the naked version"

By making small changes to the ratio of ingredients, or the temperature or processing time, they could progressively alter – and so optimise – their particles.

The result is two medicines, developed by spin-off companies, that passed rapidly through preclinical testing and into small-scale phase I clinical trials. BIND Therapeutics is trialling a tumour-hunter called BIND-014, a polymer-wrapped version of the cancer drug docetaxel. Results so far seem to show the capsules' improved seek-and-destroy abilities: those treated are responding at half the dose of the naked version. Kostarelos, who is not involved with the research, is encouraged. "The trial illustrates that actively targeted nanoparticles can offer patient benefits," he says. BIND-014 has now started phase 2 trials.

Meanwhile, Selecta Biosciences is developing a multi-component vaccine to help people quit smoking. Its controlled-release polymer sets loose an "adjuvant" that primes the immune system for action, alongside an antigen that trains immune cells to seek and destroy nicotine. The principle should work for other potential vaccines, says Farokhzad. One possibility might be to selectively shut down the overactive immune responses seen in diseases such as multiple sclerosis, without compromising the ability of the immune system to fight off infections, as existing immunosuppressant drugs do.

It is too early to say how well the vaccine does in humans, but the company recently announced a deal with pharmaceutical giant Sanofi Aventis to develop nanoparticle-based vaccines against various allergies.

In the lab, Farokhzad and Langer are extending the multi-cargo principle to cancer drugs. In one proof-of-concept study, they showed that nanocapsules loaded with two drugs – one to soften up the tumour, and one to deliver a precisely timed knockout blow – were at least five times as potent as either encapsulated drug alone.

Joseph DeSimone of the University of North Carolina, Chapel Hill, is trying a different approach. Rather than self-assembly, he is making nanoparticles in the equivalent of an ice-cube tray, giving him full control over their size and shape and a freer hand over their

All in the design

With cunning chemical engineering, drugs can be cloaked with components that protect them from the body's defences and steer them to the right place, making treatment more effective

DRUG

Active drug molecules often unleash unwanted side effects as they spread through the body

+NANOCAPSULE

Biodegradable polymers delay the active molecule's release until it approaches its target

+STEALTH CLOAK

Water-loving polymers form a shield that hides the capsule from the immune system

+ANTIBODIES

Site-specific chemical attachments allow the capsule to latch on to particular tissue, for example a tumour

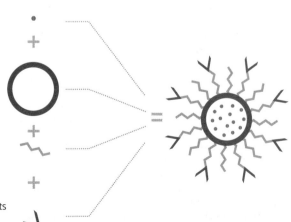

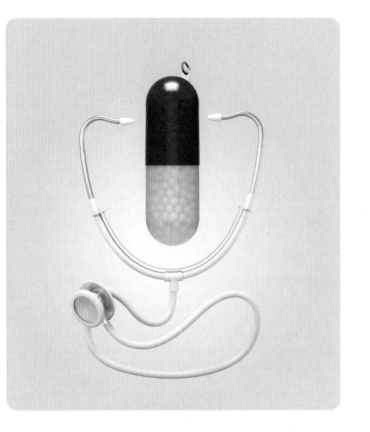

constituents. His spin-out company, Liquidia Technologies, has a seasonal flu vaccine in phase I trials, and another pharmaceutical giant, GlaxoSmithKline, is testing the technology with its own vaccines.

The moulded particles can be engineered into many sizes and shapes for different purposes. Pollen-shaped particles, for example, make a dry powder that can be inhaled rather than injected, and can also be sculpted to attract the attention of specific target cells in the body. That could provide a route to more effective vaccines against tuberculosis, a disease caused when airborne bacteria attack immune cells known as macrophages in the lungs. Inhaled vaccine particles with an affinity for macrophages could prime the cells to spew out antibody-generating antigens, allowing the immune system to recognise and deal with them in the event of a real infection.

DeSimone thinks that the uniformity of his particles compared with those formed by self-assembly could be a help when it comes to approval by regulatory agencies. "The FDA hates heterogeneity in size and shape because it means that the particles can go in different places," he says. Farokhzad points to the counterexample of Doxil, which is not made up of particles of a single size, but a uniform range. Variation could even be a boon, he says. Cancer is such a heterogeneous disease, for example in the shape and size of the blood vessel network that tumours develop, that a

treatment based on particles with a range of sizes potentially offers a better treatment.

Kostarelos says the existence of rival approaches to make encapsulated drugs can only be beneficial. "Thanks to all the different nanoparticle technologies people are exploring, acceleration of the drug approval rate is bound to happen." Tavassoli is working on alternative ways to target drugs, such as by having them home in on the extensive new blood supplies that tumours have to create. That might remove the immediate need for a protective capsule, but even so he thinks the approach could help. Before a molecule will even be considered as a potential drug, it must conform to tough criteria. For example, it must be water-soluble enough to dissolve within a cell, but hydrophobic enough to cross the lipid membranes that surround them. If you can give a capsule those properties, the active molecule doesn't have to have them, possibly making many more structures available for use.

Tracked delivery

There are more radical options out there, too. One is to design particles to catch a ride on a cancer cell's machinery for ferrying deliveries to its innards. Only once sucked inside the cell does the capsule release its payload, for instance in response to the relatively acidic environment found in tumour cells. That's what Nobuhiro Nishiyama and Kazunori

Kataoka at the University of Tokyo and their colleagues have done, using capsules loaded with a DNA-targeting anticancer drug called DACHPt and tagged with a further fluorescing molecule. By tracking the fluoresence they showed how the drug was delivered right to the doorstep of the cancer cell's nucleus, where its DNA is stored, evading the defensive proteins that drug-resistant tumour cells deploy on their periphery.

This inbuilt imaging capability is one step towards what the researchers regard as the big prize: theranostics. These are capsules that, alongside their therapeutic cargo, also carry a medical imaging payload to give doctors patient-specific diagnostic data. "Imagine being able to treat cancer, and every time you dose the patient you follow it with a test scan to show disease regression as a function of your drug delivery," says Farokhzad.

It is something he and others are already experimenting with in their labs. Adding fluorescent dyes to the capsules, or brightly fluorescing nanocrystals called quantum dots, is one possibility. These might be engineered to fluoresce only once the drug cargo is released, tracking delivery. Another avenue is to add specks of a magnetic material, such as iron oxide, so that the theranostic can be tracked using MRI scans. For a drug selectively targeting tumour cells, monitoring where they stick could reveal whether a cancer is shrinking or spreading.

Based on progress so far, Farokhzad predicts that theranostic agents will enter clinical trials within the decade. Kostarelos is also working on the idea, mainly as a tool to enable researchers to assess whether a nanocapsule is behaving as intended.

In a clinical setting, though, Kostarelos is less convinced of the need to combine so many functions in one drug. "The more complicated they get, the less attractive they are to pharmaceutical companies and the regulatory authorities," he says. It becomes more difficult, and more expensive, to make a commercial product that is reliably safe in all situations.

Although Farokhzad does not disagree, he points out that commercialisation always lags behind innovation. "If we can be equally innovative as to the way that these particles are manufactured, there is no reason why they shouldn't ultimately appear in the clinic," he says. In the meantime, nanocapsule weapons will be judged not by how cleverly they are designed, but whether they help win the war against disease. "If you're a patient with cancer, that's all you really care about – to get better," says Farokhzad. ■

Cure-all no more

The world's favourite over-the-counter pain remedy, paracetamol, has a dark side, finds Tiffany O'Callaghan

YOU'VE got a terrible headache. Niggling knee pain. An aching back. What do you reach for? Chances are that you'll open your medicine cabinet and grab some paracetamol. Half an hour or so later, you'll feel a lot better. Or will you?

Paracetamol, also known as acetaminophen, is the cure-all of our age, used to treat everything from sprained ankles to toothaches and even labour pain. It is on the first rung of the World Health Organization's "analgesic ladder", which doctors use to treat cancer pain. We spoon it to our children to fight fever; as adults we pop it to relieve headaches or period cramps, and as we get older we're prescribed it to soothe arthritis or backache. In the US, 27 billion doses of the drug are sold each year, and it is found in more than 600 products.

Given its ubiquity, you might assume that paracetamol is safe and effective – at least at the recommended dose. That's why we lean on it more than aspirin or ibuprofen, which can irritate the stomach lining and cause bleeding. But as it turns out, this stalwart of the medicine cabinet is not quite as reliably gentle as you might think.

Paracetamol was discovered in the late 19th century, but it was rejected almost immediately because of a bizarre side effect: it seemed to turn some people blue (see timeline, page 40). That was probably because of contamination with a different drug, but as a result paracetamol was sidelined until the 1940s, when further tests showed it was good at reducing fever. Later studies concluded that it was a pretty effective painkiller too. But it really took off in the 1960s, in response to emerging concerns about the long-term side effects of aspirin and other non-steroidal anti-inflammatory drugs (NSAIDs). Estimates of NSAID-related deaths a year just in people with arthritis vary from 3200 to around 16,500 in the US.

Paracetamol, on the other hand, we think of as relatively safe. Sure, if you take lots of tablets it could seriously damage your liver, but at the recommended dose, it's fine, right?

This assumption is now being challenged by research suggesting that, when taken for prolonged periods, it may damage the stomach as much as NSAIDs. That might be an acceptable risk in exchange for pain relief, but in many of those who take it, paracetamol barely works better than a placebo.

Mysterious drug

How could this be? The fact is, despite its ubiquity, we still don't really understand how paracetamol works. A leading theory is that, in part, it works like aspirin and ibuprofen, by blocking enzymes known as cyclooxygenases. These enzymes are responsible for making hormone-like compounds called prostaglandins, which trigger pain and swelling in the body as well as stimulating production of the mucus that shields our stomachs against digestive acids. NSAIDs halt the swelling process, but leave the stomach vulnerable. The suspicion was that paracetamol inhibited cyclooxygenases, but to a much lesser extent; it doesn't reduce inflammation as these other drugs do.

Although studies in the past decade have hinted that long-term use of paracetamol might trigger internal bleeding, these findings were widely dismissed by critics who cited shortcomings of the study designs. In 2011, however, Michael Doherty of Nottingham City Hospital, UK, published a study that was harder to ignore. He followed the progress of 892 men and women with the niggling knee pain that often sets in at middle-age – usually an early symptom of osteoarthritis. Some were given paracetamol, others ibuprofen, while a third and fourth group took either a high or low-dose combination of the two.

Paracetamol is the first drug most doctors turn to for patients with such symptoms, but when Doherty looked at the blood results of those taking it, he was shocked: levels of haemoglobin, the protein that carries oxygen in the blood, were dropping fast. What's more, their red blood cells were growing smaller and paler. The most logical explanation was that they were losing blood internally, and significant quantities of it. After three months, a fifth of them seemed to have lost the equivalent of an entire unit of blood (about 400 millilitres). That was the same amount as those taking ibuprofen – only the ibuprofen group reported feeling less pain.

In those combining high doses of both paracetamol and ibuprofen, the haemoglobin loss after three months was even more startling: 7 per cent of the people in that group lost the amount of haemoglobin you would find in two units of blood. The upshot: when taken for long periods, paracetamol may be just as damaging to the stomach lining as NSAID drugs are.

"The horrifying aspect of this is that people look at me and say 'it's over the counter, it must be safe'," says Kay Brune, a professor of pharmacology and toxicology at the University of Erlangen-Nuremberg in Germany. Brune has been campaigning to have paracetamol removed from over-the-counter sale in Germany, but has so far been unsuccessful. "Before, physicians simply said 'OK, if it doesn't work, it may not do any harm'. But now we know it can do harm," he says. ▶

The rise of paracetamol

Early 1880s: German doctors accidentally give a patient a recently synthesised chemical, acetanilide: his fever drops dramatically

1886 Acetanilide sold under the trade name Antifebrin. Successful, despite turning some people's lips and skin blue

1893 German physiologist Joseph von Mering discovers the acetanilide derivative, N-acetyl-p-aminophenol (paracetamol) but thinks it is too toxic. It still turns people blue

1947 Paracetamol is rediscovered by physiologists at Yale University. Reduces pain and fever, without the side effects of acetanilide. Original observations of toxicity assumed to be down to contamination

Internal bleeding isn't the only issue that's keeping drug regulators on their toes. In January 2014, the US Food and Drug Administration asked manufacturers to stop producing prescription drugs containing more than 325 milligrams of paracetamol per tablet because of the risk of accidental overdose. Paracetamol poisoning is responsible for nearly 80,000 visits to the emergency room in the US each year, and a third of these are people who overdosed accidentally.

Although pill packets clearly state that the maximum recommended dose is no more than 3 or 4 grams spread over 24 hours (or six to eight 500 mg tablets), because of paracetamol's reputation for safety, some people take more than this. "They know they're not supposed to take maybe six or eight tablets at a time, but they have a toothache and they just don't want to go to the dentist," says Daniel Budnitz at the US Centers for Disease Control in Atlanta, Georgia, who has studied overdose cases.

If you regularly exceed 4 grams, you can quickly enter dangerous territory. During the breakdown of paracetamol, a toxin is produced that has to be mopped up by a specific enzyme in the liver, and if you take too much too fast, the supply of that enzyme quickly dwindles.

As little as 5 to 7.5 g per day can cause serious liver complications in otherwise healthy people. For people with compromised liver function due to alcoholism or liver disease, a harmful dose can be lower still. And despite the fact that the recommended maximum dose is no more than 4 g per day, roughly 6 per cent of US adults – about 14 million people – are routinely prescribed more than this, often in prescriptions that combine the drug with opioids to treat severe pain.

Do these risks matter? Because of the huge numbers of people who take paracetamol, and the relative ease with which it is purchased and consumed, even small risks become significant. Even so, paracetamol is valued by medical authorities – not just for treating life's little hurts, but for persistent and potentially debilitating conditions. The UK's National Institute for Health and Care Excellence (NICE), the body that sets standards for medical practice, recommends paracetamol as the first-choice drug for treating the chronic pain associated with conditions like osteoarthritis and lower back

pain. The American College of Rheumatology also recommends it for arthritis.

In the US, an estimated 43 million people take paracetamol each week, and nearly two-thirds of them take the drug routinely for longer than six months.

If paracetamol were effective against chronic pain, you might consider the trade-off worthwhile, but the drug has been found seriously wanting. A review of research that

"Why are we bothering to give a drug to people that's toxic, when it often doesn't work?"

looked at people taking paracetamol to relieve chronic joint pain found seven studies that compared the drug with a placebo. Five of these found it to be marginally more effective, but two found no difference.

"Why are we bothering to give a drug to people that's toxic, that has significant potential problems, when it doesn't work?" asks Andrew Moore, an anaesthetist and director of pain research at the University of Oxford. "It's unethical."

Of course, placebos can themselves make people feel better: another review of placebo-controlled trials for treating joint pain found that many people experienced moderate relief from sham treatment, particularly when it was given as an injection. For ethical reasons, doctors don't usually prescribe placebos, so the safest active pill is often the next best thing.

"Is paracetamol a safe placebo?" asks John Dickson, a rheumatologist with the Redcar and Cleveland Primary Care Trust in the UK, and a consulting clinician for the 2008 NICE guidelines. "The work Doherty did shows it is not."

In March 2014, the Osteoarthritis Research Society International changed its paracetamol guidelines to "uncertain" to reflect growing safety concerns. And for a while at least, it looked like these concerns would be similarly heeded in the UK. When NICE issued new draft

How effective is your painkiller?

When it comes to relieving acute pain, such as a headache, sprain or post-operative pain, not all drugs are equal

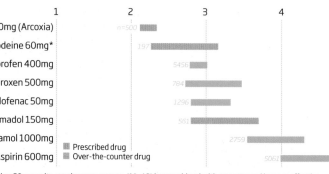

Number of people who would have to take a drug for one of them to experience a 50% reduction in pain over 4-6 hours (smaller number = better) *Data sets vary in size*

Etoricoxib 120mg (Arcoxia)	n=500
Paracetamol 1000mg + Codeine 60mg*	197
Ibuprofen 400mg	5456
Naproxen 500mg	784
Diclofenac 50mg	1296
Tramadol 150mg	561
Paracetamol 1000mg	2759
Aspirin 600mg	5061

■ Prescribed drug
■ Over-the-counter drug

*Codeine 60mg on its own has a poor score (11-48) but combined with paracetamol is more effective

SOURCE: THE OXFORD LEAGUE TABLE OF ANALGESIC EFFICACY

Timeline (top of page)

1955/56 Paracetamol sold in the US as Tylenol and in the UK as Panadol

1962 Concerns surface about stomach bleeding and ulcers associated with NSAIDs and aspirin. Paracetamol sales boosted

1966 Reports of severe liver damage from intentional overdose with paracetamol

1982 Discovery that aspirin puts small children at increased risk of Reye's syndrome

2011 Study suggests paracetamol causes reductions in haemoglobin similar to ibuprofen

2013 In the UK, draft guidelines from NICE recommend removing paracetamol as first-line treatment for osteoarthritis

2014 Final NICE guidelines, keep paracetamol as first-line treatment for osteoarthritis

---

guidelines for osteoarthritis in August 2013, it did away with the recommendation of paracetamol as a first resort, and flagged its potential dangers. "On balance, the risks of paracetamol outweigh the benefits of any gain in symptom control," the report read.

Yet by the time the final version was published the following February, the old advice had been reinstated. This was partly down to objections raised by doctors about having few alternative options, though NICE says it is also awaiting the results of a more comprehensive review of over-the-counter painkillers by the UK's Medicines and Healthcare Products Regulatory Agency. Dickson, like others, was disappointed. "If paracetamol isn't safe, we shouldn't be prescribing it," he says.

Of course, most of us don't take paracetamol every day; it's a drug we reach for when we develop a headache or sprain an ankle. And for acute pain of that nature, paracetamol performs reasonably well, if not as spectacularly as its popularity might suggest. Pharmacists measure the effectiveness of painkillers by looking at whether they can reduce your reported sensation of pain by at least 50 per cent, and by counting how many people would need to take it for one person to experience this level of relief compared with placebo. This is known as the number needed to treat (NNT).

Effective relief

For example, in the case of the moderate pain of a sprained ankle, 3.8 people would need to take a standard 1 g dose of paracetamol (2 tablets) for one of them to get effective relief. For a standard 400-milligram dose of ibuprofen, the NNT is 2.5 (see table, left).

Most people suffering from acute pain are unlikely to take these drugs for more than a few days, so the risk of internal bleeding is less of a concern than in those taking it for prolonged periods. But, given that paracetamol isn't as effective as some

So many painkillers: which to choose?

alternatives for short-term pain, it could make more sense to take one of them, or a combination of drugs that work through different pathways, such as paracetamol plus ibuprofen.

Should we do away with paracetamol entirely? Most experts believe it's still a useful tool in the arsenal against fevers, headaches and sore muscles because, in the people for whom it does work, it tends to work fairly well. It's just that, as with many analgesics, the chances are hit-and-miss that it will work for you – possibly because everyone's body is slightly different.

However, when it comes to chronic pain, it could be time for a rethink. Moore suggests measuring your pain, tracking whether a drug makes a difference, and if it doesn't, quickly moving on. "Frankly, with paracetamol, if it's not going to work within a week, it's never going to work with you," he says.

Indeed, a spokeswoman for McNeil Consumer Healthcare, which makes Tylenol in the US, points out that the drug's label clearly states that consumers should stop use and ask a doctor if they have pain that gets worse or lasts more than 10 days.

Of course, the ideal would be to develop a

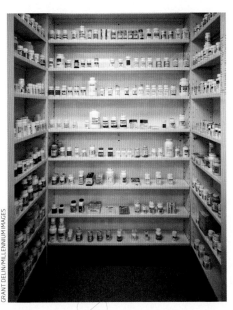

paracetamol variant that worked better and had fewer drawbacks. Stuart Bevan and David Andersson at King's College London recently found that when paracetamol is given, one of its breakdown products activates a protein on the surface of nerves in the spinal cord and reduces their ability to transmit pain signals. If confirmed, targeting this protein could be a promising starting point.

Pharmaceutical companies are also researching and developing new analgesics. But given the huge regulatory hurdles for over-the-counter drugs, few are focusing on that market. "It is more likely that medicines currently available on prescription would become available over the counter, as they will already have a good amount of safety data," says Roger Knaggs at the University of Nottingham, UK.

Still, it's possible that a promising alternative already exists. Just as paracetamol was consigned to a dusty back room for half a century, other analgesics may have been overlooked or condemned for the wrong reasons. Safety hurdles today are much higher than when drugs like paracetamol were first approved. If it were a new drug, says Moore, it probably wouldn't get approval.

It could also be that some drugs which fail to win approval are doing so because of poor study design, rather than serious flaws with the drugs themselves. Robert Dworkin at the University of Rochester in New York, is the director of an initiative with the FDA that is taking a second look at analgesics that didn't pass muster in earlier clinical trials. It is currently focused on prescription-strength drugs, but Dworkin says a similar approach could work for over-the-counter remedies too.

In the meantime, what should you do with the paracetamol in your own cupboard? For short-lived aches and pains, the advice hasn't changed much. "If you follow the instructions and if you don't take it in too-large doses, paracetamol is very safe," says Bevan.

But for ongoing pain, it may be time to start looking for alternatives. With any drug, there's a risk that side effects will outweigh benefits. For paracetamol, we need to decide which risks are still worth taking. ■

GRANT DELIN/MILLENNIUM IMAGES

Drugs with bite

Venoms may not be the most obvious source of medicines but they are the hottest ticket in pharmaceuticals, says **James Mitchell Crow**

A BRUSH with a pit viper is not a relaxing experience. They are venomous, can grow to several metres long and will be on to you long before you know they are there, sensing your body heat with a pair of highly sensitive infrared-detecting organs that sit just below their eyes. Bumping into one of these creatures in their native forests in South America would not be good for anyone's heart, so it is ironic that pit viper venom has given us a drug used to treat high blood pressure.

In fact, the toxic mixtures of chemicals we call venoms have a long history as medical treatments. From poisonous toads to toxic tarantulas, venomous animals provide ingredients for traditional medicines around the world. Unlikely as it sounds, venoms have many of the attributes a good drug needs. When a venomous animal pounces on its prey, the chemicals it injects must be stable enough to travel around the victim's body and

able to evade its defences until they reach their site of action, when they must hit the target with exquisite selectivity and minimum side effects. Millennia of evolution have honed venoms to achieve exactly what a doctor hopes an injected drug will do.

Nevertheless, western medicine has had difficulties cashing in on this natural asset. In 1981, captopril, a drug based on pit viper venom, became the first venom-derived drug to be approved by the US Food and Drug Administration. In the following two decades pharmaceutical companies produced a slow trickle of other such drugs. Now, however, this trickle looks set to turn into a steady stream as venom research enters the genomics age, turning the once-laborious job of sifting through toxic cocktails for potential cures into a high-throughput process. As a result, venom is one of the hottest commodities in pharmaceuticals. *New Scientist* surveys what it has to offer.

DRUG: *Captopril*
SOURCE: *Pit viper*
CONDITION: *Hypertension*

How does deadly pit viper venom work as a drug? It's all a question of quantity. "Every medicine is also a poison – the effect depends on the dose," says Bryan Fry, who researches venomous animals and their evolution at the University of Queensland in Brisbane, Australia. "The snake kills by dropping its target's blood pressure through the floor," he says. "To use the venom as a drug, you just give less of it."

Pit viper venom provided more than just the original venom-based drug, though. It is also intimately tied up with the discovery of how the body regulates blood pressure. In the late 1960s, this mechanism was still something of a mystery, confounding efforts to manipulate it. Among those working to understand it was John Vane, a pharmacologist at the Royal College of Surgeons of England. The breakthrough came when a Brazilian postdoctoral researcher, Sérgio Ferreira, joined Vane's group. Ferreira had been studying the venom of a pit viper native to Brazil, *Bothrops jararaca*, and he brought a sample of it with him. The team discovered that a toxic peptide in the venom would selectively inhibit the action of angiotensin-converting enzyme (ACE), a chemical suspected of playing a role in the regulation of blood pressure.

During the following decade, the role of ACE in boosting blood pressure by controlling the release of water and salts from the kidneys became clear – as did the therapeutic value of blocking it. Captopril, a synthetic analogue of the snake venom peptide, was first made in 1975, and hit the clinic just six years later. It was the founder member of what is now a family of ACE-inhibitor drugs.

Most of the venom-derived drugs approved since captopril also originated in snakes, mainly because snake venoms are the easiest to work with. Compared with a scorpion or a spider, say, snakes produce a vast volume of venom, making them easier to analyse. Snake venom is also a much simpler cocktail than that produced by many other animals: a spider's venom can contain over 1000 peptides, whereas a snake's venom might contain only 25.

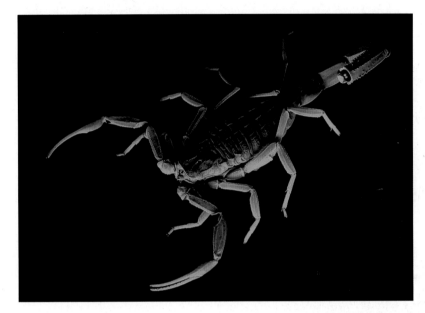

The deathstalker scorpion is useful in the fight against cancer

DRUG: *Chlorotoxin*
SOURCE: *Deathstalker scorpion*
CONDITION: *Cancer*

Radioactive scorpion venom might sound like the stuff comic-book villains would use. In fact it is an experimental anticancer drug in clinical trials. The venom in question comes from the deathstalker scorpion (*Leiurus quinquestriatus*), a bright yellow beast native to north Africa and the Middle East. As the name suggests, its sting can be fatal.

Within that sting lies a peptide called chlorotoxin, which has an unusual property – it sticks strongly to tumour cells while ignoring surrounding healthy tissue, by binding to a cancer-specific protein called matrix metalloproteinase-2. This tumour-targeting makes it a promising ally in the fight against cancer. Load up chlorotoxin with a radioisotope, for example, and it will deliver its radioactive payload straight to a tumour. This approach has been investigated by TransMolecular, a company based in Cambridge,

Massachusetts, as a way to treat glioma, a form of brain cancer. Chlorotoxin passed a phase II clinical trial in 2009.

More recently, the peptide has become the key ingredient in an experimental surgical tool called Tumor Paint. When chlorotoxin is tagged with a fluorescent dye, it will illuminate a tumour – a trick that makes the surgeon's job easier by helping to pinpoint cancerous growth and ensure that all the cancerous cells are removed and healthy tissue spared.

Chlorotoxin's performance through the early stages of clinical trials did not go unnoticed. In April 2011, TransMolecular's tumour-targeter was snapped up by biopharmaceutical company Morphotek, a US-based subsidiary of Japanese drug giant Eisai. Though the company has not revealed its plans for chlorotoxin, spokesman Terry Cushmore said in 2012 that they intend to refine it before taking it into further clinical studies. "We are reconfiguring the peptide to enhance its utility for diagnosis and treatment of a wide range of cancer types, based on the clinical findings of the earlier studies." ❯

DRUG: *Conotoxin*
SOURCE: *Cone snail*
CONDITION: *Severe pain*

Divers beware – not all pretty seashells are harmless. Pick up one containing a live cone snail and it will defend itself with its sting. The result can be fatal. Nevertheless, venom researcher Richard Lewis and his team at the University of Queensland in Brisbane, Australia, seek out these creatures along the Great Barrier Reef. "They're a challenge to get," he says. "During the day they hide, and you can turn hundreds of pieces of dead coral over before you find a cone snail."

It is worth the hunt. Cone snails are one of the youngsters of the venom world, developing their poisonous sting just a few tens of millions of years ago. As a result, their venoms are still an evolutionary work in progress. Members of the same species can deploy very different mixtures of chemicals. "Even individuals collected from the same place may only have a 25 per cent overlap in the venoms they produce," says Lewis. That means they produce a vast array of potential medicines.

Whereas snakes tend to target the cardiovascular system, cone snails prefer to shut down the nervous system of their prey. This means their venom has great potential as the next generation of pain medication.

Indeed, conotoxins have been found to be about 100 times as effective in relieving nerve pain as morphine. "In our initial safety study, we tested the drug in more than 30 people with severe cancer pain, and the compound was able to produce a really quite profound reversal of pain in many of these patients, an effect that could last for many days with a single injection," says Lewis.

One conotoxin, zicotinide, is already in the clinic. But it can only be injected directly into the spine, so a team led by Lewis's colleague David Craik has developed a range of synthetic conotoxins that they hope will be more useful. A drug that can be taken orally is now showing promise in rats and could enter clinical trials soon.

"Cone snail venoms shut down the nervous system, making them potential painkillers"

DRUG: *Cobratoxin*
SOURCE: *Cobra*
CONDITION: *Multiple sclerosis, HIV*

Snake venom has a place in several ancient medical traditions. As early as the 1930s western pharmacists began testing cobra venom as a treatment for conditions ranging from asthma to multiple sclerosis. But in recent years, modern techniques from mass spectrometry to high-throughput lab-on-a-chip bioassays have made life easier. Chemists can pick out and identify the specific venom components with beneficial effects, eliminating some unpleasant side effects and making the whole process safer.

One such component is showing promise for treating multiple sclerosis. Quite what triggers MS remains unknown. What is clear, though, is that the body's immune system begins to attack the insulating sheath that protects nerve cells, causing damage that can progressively impair sensory and cognitive function and movement. Bringing the immune system back into balance has proved very difficult, but a venom chemical called cobratoxin might help.

In 2011, Florida-based firm ReceptoPharm had a patent approved for a version of cobratoxin chemically modified to remove its toxicity. The company claimed that its modified peptide halted the development of MS in 90 per cent of laboratory rats with the rodent equivalent of the condition. The peptide seems to stimulate the release of a messenger molecule called interleukin-27, which puts the brakes on an overactive immune response, bringing immune activity back down toward normal levels. The company is still studying the peptide, dubbed RPI-78M, with a view to eventual human trials.

Meanwhile, a related cobratoxin molecule has shown promise in treating HIV. A modified version of the toxin seems to impede the spread of the virus by blocking receptors on the surface of the body's immune cells – the same receptors that the virus would otherwise latch on to before infecting the body's immune cells.

Cone snails have to be collected with tongs as their sting can kill

NORBERT WU/MINDEN PICTURES/FLPA

DRUG: *ShK-186*
SOURCE: *Sea anemone*
CONDITION: *Autoimmune disease*

In the warm, shallow waters of the Caribbean Sea, especially in the coral reefs around Cuba, lives a species of sea anemone called *Stichodactyla helianthus*. In the early 1990s a group of Cuban researchers on a diving expedition collected some specimens to analyse their toxins. The compound they discovered spawned an experimental drug, ShK, that has the potential to treat a broad range of autoimmune diseases.

These diseases arise when the immune system mistakenly decides that one of the body's own tissues is foreign and begins to attack it. In many cases the damage is caused by a particular group of immune cells called effector memory T-cells. These possess a unique ion channel called a Kv1.3 potassium channel without which they cannot function, and it is this channel that ShK targets. "ShK puts the cork in the bottle," says Ray Norton at Monash University in Melbourne, Australia, whose involvement with the project began in 1996. "In the presence of our compound, the cells become immobilised and wither and die."

The compound was refined to make it target potassium channels more specifically, and one version, ShK-186, is now in early human trials for treating psoriasis. The company developing it, Kineta, says it has potential to treat other autoimmune diseases, including type 1 diabetes and rheumatoid arthritis.

Quite what such a compound is doing in sea anemones in the first place is an open question. Possibly it acts to stun the fish that they eat, or protect them from predators. Ion channel function can vary significantly from species to species, and the ion channel's role in fish could be very different from its role in our bodies.

"Until recently the gila monster was thought to be one of just two venomous lizards"

The gila monster's venom contains an anti-diabetes drug

DRUG: *Exenatide (Byetta)*
SOURCE: *Gila monster*
CONDITION: *Type 2 diabetes*

A bite from a gila monster will really mess with your metabolism. Fortunately these lizards, found in the deserts of the US Southwest, are large and lumbering and most humans can easily outpace them. Nevertheless, each year a handful of people get close enough to discover that the gila monster's bite delivers a painful cocktail of chemicals that causes nausea, fever and faintness – and can even induce a heart attack.

However, within the venom lies a very useful compound. Called exendin 4, it triggers one of the body's insulin-releasing pathways. This effect makes it ideal for treating type 2 diabetes, a condition in which insufficient insulin is produced to keep glucose levels in check. A synthetic version of exendin 4, called exenatide, was approved as an anti-diabetes drug by the US Food and Drug Administration in 2005. Now the compound is being investigated for its anti-obesity properties as well, since it also slows stomach emptying,

reinforcing feelings of fullness after eating.

Until around a decade ago, the gila monster was thought to be one of just two venomous lizards – the other being the closely related beaded lizard found in nearby Mexico. We now know that lizards and snakes share a common venomous ancestor, and that many lizards – from iguanas to komodo dragons – which were never suspected of being venomous, come equipped with venom glands.

Research into lizard venom has barely begun, so it may be a while before any other lizard-based medicine hits the pharmacy. But the wait could be worth it, says Bryan Fry at the University of Queensland in Brisbane, Australia, who researches lizard toxin evolution. "If you want to find something useful, then the more novel the venomous animal, the more novel its venom." And that gives the best drug leads, he says. "I think it is one of the strongest arguments we have for preserving biodiversity." ∎

Going to extremes

As antibiotic resistance increases, the hunt for new medicines is turning to the ocean depths. Not a moment too soon, says **Jon White**

THE 150-kilometre trip out from Chile won't be comfortable. It will be hot, choppy and take all night. Travelling across this patch of the Pacific Ocean, you run afoul of both El Niño and La Niña, whose perpetual tug of war with the weather can make even the most stoic seafarers lose their lunch.

Luckily, once the crew – an eclectic mix of hardened South American mariners and British salvage engineers – reach their destination, they should find placid waters. That will make it a lot easier for the engines to steady the ship's position. They certainly can't use an anchor: out here, the ocean floor is 8 kilometres down, a treacherous abyss known as the Peru-Chile trench. But what the team haul out of these depths could save your life.

The Peru-Chile trench is the first stop in an international raid on the unexplored recesses of the oceans, organised by Marcel Jaspars, a chemist at the University of Aberdeen in the UK. The exotic organisms that thrive there could be pressed into service against some of our worst enemies, from cancer to drug-resistant bacteria. There's not much time to lose. Without them, some say we may be heading for an antibiotics apocalypse.

We have always relied on nature to fill our medicine cabinets. Over half of all drugs on the market are either derived from or inspired by plants, animals or bacteria – aspirin is extracted from the bark of the willow tree, penicillin comes from a fungus, and we have soil bacteria to thank for many antibiotics.

Some of these discoveries were happy accidents, but traditionally pharmaceutical companies went foraging for medicinal treasures in remote locations – a practice known as bioprospecting. Such expeditions have struck gold in the past: vinblastine, a chemotherapy drug used to treat Hodgkin's lymphoma, is derived from the rosy periwinkle, a plant native to Madagascar.

Out of time

But over the past 20 years, conventional bioprospecting has seen diminishing returns, particularly among microorganisms. The same thing keeps happening; bioprospectors find a promising candidate, companies spend small fortunes on development – only to find that everyone has wasted their time. This is happening even as our need for new antibiotics grows steadily more urgent, says Laura Piddock, a microbiologist at the University of Birmingham, UK, who directs a global initiative to develop new antibiotics.

Antibiotic-resistant strains of gonorrhoea, tuberculosis and *Staphylococcus aureus* are on the rise. Such bacteria have evolved resistance mechanisms even against the antibiotics of last resort. Within a decade or two, they will have become resistant to all major antibiotics, and simple infections will become fatal. But no new organisms have been found on which to base better drugs. "The pipeline is pretty empty," Piddock says (see chart, page 48).

Desperate for new compounds, pharmaceutical firms turned to synthetic analogues. But these have not equalled the natural diversity that has evolved over billions of years. The effect has been fewer products, not more, says Guy Carter, an industry consultant in New York.

But Jaspars is convinced nature still has a few tricks up her sleeve. The organisms that flourish in the comfort zone of Earth's biosphere make up only a fraction of life on our planet. Outside what we consider the habitable regions – in the desiccated soils of deserts or buried beneath thick ice or rock – creatures not only survive, but thrive, at extremes of temperature, salinity and darkness.

We first realised that their unusual adaptive chemistry could be used to our advantage about 40 years ago. Thomas Brock – at the time a microbiologist at the University of Washington – was driving through Yellowstone National Park on his way back to the lab. The hot pools and geysers proved too tempting; he stopped to admire them and returned to the lab with a water sample. He was stunned to discover life thriving in the near-boiling liquid. So began a decade of study of thermally resistant microbes. One species, *Thermus aquaticus*, turned out to make an enzyme, taq polymerase, that was key to automating methods used to amplify small amounts of ❯

The world's most hostile environments house more life than anyone suspected

Drilling into Lake Ellsworth, West Antarctica, hunting for signs of life

P. BUCKTROUT/BRITISH ANTARCTIC SURVEY

DNA. It turned a tricky, labour-intensive process into one doable on any lab bench, effectively ushering in the genomics revolution.

It wasn't until a few years ago that we began to realise that these adaptations could also be turned against some of our nastiest medical foes. Fungi discovered in the acidic lakes of Lechuguilla Cave in New Mexico – whose metal-infused waters should have stymied all life – tipped us off (see diagram, page 49). One hardy strain of *Penicillium* produces a compound that inhibits the growth of lung cancer cells. Another compound, berkelic acid, isolated from fungus and bacteria found living in the toxic water of an open pit mine, slowed ovarian cancer cell growth by 50 per cent. The hunt was on to unearth more of nature's extreme medicines.

But if we thought life would be rare in such spots, we were in for a surprise. Microbiologist Alan Bull of the University of Kent, UK, has scoured the driest and highest desert on Earth: the Atacama, which straddles northern Chile. Microbes there face desiccation and intense bombardment by ultraviolet light; the environment is so punishing that NASA has used it as an analogue for Mars. Here, Bull hoped to find his favourite microbial group: actinobacteria, rich in the molecules that are essentially ready-made medicines, small enough to slip through the body's defences.

He expected to find a few hardy species barely eking out a grim living. But at last count, Bull and his colleagues had collected 1000 cultures. Some pump out compounds with antibiotic, anticancer and anti-inflammatory properties. Some are familiar. Many are not. "The majority are likely to be new species whose medical potential is virtually untouched," Bull says.

The desert isn't the only place revealing an unexpected cornucopia. Antarctica, another vast, underexplored region, has been opening up for bioprospectors, aided by an unexpected ally – climate change. David Pearce at the

Northumbria University, UK, has been analysing samples taken from sediment beneath the subglacial waters of Hodgson Lake. The lake is emerging from under what was a very thick ice cap thanks to deglaciation, allowing the first recovery of 100,000-year-old Antarctic subglacial sediment. What the team found echoed Bull's findings: the biomass was higher than he expected. "Perhaps the selective pressures aren't as severe as we once thought," Pearce says. "It looks as if it might be quite conducive to life."

More importantly, these weren't just many members of a few species. Genomics revealed that the lake site was teeming with diversity. "We might have expected there to be highly specialised organisms," Pearce says. "But we found a very diverse range; some freshwater, some marine, some extremophilic, some more

cosmopolitan – that was quite a surprise."

That diversity was also represented in the biochemical make-up of the organisms. DNA analysis showed that about a quarter of the biological material present at Hodgson Lake couldn't be matched to any known sequences. The group is awaiting final results, but it seems that these are brand new species.

If life at extreme temperatures was thought to struggle, it was believed to be entirely non-existent in the rocks deep beneath our feet. But in the past few years, we have been proven wrong yet again. The rocky depths harbour yet another other vast microbial ecosystem that is as untapped as Antarctica and spans pretty much the entire globe.

Into the deep

Everywhere we have looked, microbial life has surprised us with its tenacity, versatility and abundance. But perhaps no extreme environment is more unexplored – or more promising – than the ocean trenches. While we have made large leaps in understanding deep-sea life, the trenches are the last unknown, says Tim Shank, a deep-sea biologist at Woods Hole Oceanographic Institution in Massachusetts. "It's the largest unexplored biome on Earth," he says.

"Ocean trenches are pretty unique places," says Jaspars. Here, the so-called hadal zone combines several extremes at once: immense pressure, total darkness and temperatures down to 2 °C – a temperature that, while not obviously extreme, stifles most bacterial growth. Punishing environment aside, the trenches' isolated nature and unique ecology make them underwater versions of the Galapagos Islands. Each should hold a rainbow of unique life that has had to adapt to its unusual home.

In 2013, Jaspars's hunch that deep trenches hold rich life was verified: microbial ecologist Ronnie Glud and his team at the University of Southern Denmark in Odense revealed the results of an analysis of samples collected from Challenger Deep at the bottom of the Mariana trench, nearly 11 kilometres below the surface of the western Pacific. Every cubic centimetre of mud brought back contained, on average, 10 million microbes – about 10 times more than in mud collected from a plateau at the top of the trench. How could these light-deprived organisms be so prolific? Glud says that the trenches are particularly good at capturing life-supporting nutrients. Their broad, steep slopes act as a funnel to channel organic matter down to the bottom,

Antibiotic apocalypse

In 2013, antibiotic-resistant MRSA killed more people in the US than AIDS, hepatitis B and tuberculosis combined. Within a decade or two, these bacteria will become resistant to all major antibiotics

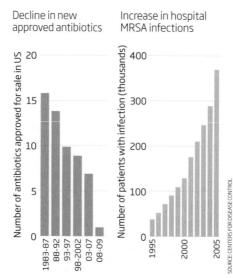

Decline in new approved antibiotics

Increase in hospital MRSA infections

SOURCE: CENTERS FOR DISEASE CONTROL

where it feeds the waiting bacteria.

But would trench organisms also contain possible new medicines? Early hints came when Jaspars collaborated with Bull on chemicals isolated from a different cluster of Mariana trench microbes. *Dermacoccus abyssi*, an actinobacterium hauled from the seabed by a Japanese remotely operated submarine, produces dermacozines, a never-before-seen family of biochemicals that are showing promise in several areas, including as a cancer treatment and against the parasite that causes sleeping sickness.

The Peru-Chile trench, says Jaspars, should hold a similar population of novel bacteria – and no one has ever looked for them. "Only two or three samples have ever been taken there," he says. But bacteria weren't on the shopping list of those collectors: that project was after worms and other small organisms. "What they found was pretty unusual and different," Jaspars says. "So we have good evidence that that will be the case for us."

Jaspars had his work cut out for him. After all, these trenches have remained unexplored for good reason – it's been all but impossible to reach them. So with £9.5 million in funding from the European Union to begin his bold project – dubbed PharmaSea – Jaspars got to work. He assembled his partners carefully: spanning 13 countries and comprising 25 institutions and commercial groups, they would be an all-star team. Chile was chosen

for its access to the trench; other partners for their expertise. British salvage firm Deep Tek have created a novel combination of rope and winch that, its designers hope, will eliminate the need for specialist scientific ships and thereby cut sampling costs by a factor of 10.

But there's one obstacle that is not so easy to negotiate. For the creatures that call this hostile terrain home, our temperate environment is every bit as deadly as their home is to us. Tracy Mincer, also at Woods

"Ocean trenches' isolation and unique ecology makes them underwater versions of the Galapagos Islands"

Hole, points out that many are likely to be piezophiles – pressure-sensitive organisms that need a crushing environment to thrive. These deep-water bacteria may not survive their journey to the surface.

A handful of sophisticated high-pressure chambers allow researchers to grow small quantities of these extremophiles, but such equipment is rare and tricky to use. Luckily, Jaspars has got his hands on a chamber that can simulate a depth of 4000 metres, which should help keep some of the less hardy bacteria on life support. But he will be sampling from a range of depths,

and thinks some of these bugs can adapt to sea-level pressures.

Only when the samples have been safely retrieved and placed into cold storage can the long road from deep-ocean gloop to new drug begin. The PharmaSea team hopes to get several drug candidates into animal testing by the time the project finishes.

First they will isolate the bacteria and coax them into larger colonies. Then they will make an extract of the bacteria and pit the hundreds of compounds they produce against cells infected with various diseases. "If something is a match, you purify until you have the active chemical and test that further," Jaspars says.

Some cutting-edge screening methods will help speed up the process. To find activity against diseases of the nervous system, for example, Jaspars recruited researchers at the Catholic University of Leuven (KUL) in Belgium, who have developed novel zebrafish assays. Zebrafish are unexpectedly good animals on which to test new medicines as they have genetic, physiological and pharmacological similarities with humans. Most importantly, using the fish means screening is fast and can be done with small samples.

The final stop will be large-scale development by a pharmaceutical company. While big pharma may have largely stepped back from antibiotics, smaller firms are venturing into that territory. Ronald Farquhar, who leads drug discovery efforts at Cubist Pharmaceuticals of Lexington, Massachusetts, is enthusiastic about PharmaSea's prospects. "Diverse and exotic environments are vital to finding new classes of antibiotics," he says.

Pharmasea's visit to the Pacific depths will be followed by similar trips to other ocean trenches: the Kermadec off New Zealand, the Mariana in the western Pacific and the Izu-Bonin off Japan.

But first, the Peru-Chile trench beckons. After a few delays, such as difficulties with generating a rope more than 9 kilometres long, the ship will depart in July 2015. Once in place, Deep Tek engineers will drop a metre-long coring device over the side. It will take 4 to 6 hours for the apparatus to sink down to the seabed and dig itself into the sediment. The journey up, powered by motors, will be faster. During their 10 days sampling the trench, the engineers will work round-the-clock shifts to collect the cores.

Everyone on board hopes the precious cargo they transport back to the mainland will usher in a new dawn of medical miracles – courtesy of the microscopic life that's been biding its time in Earth's extremes for millions of years. ∎

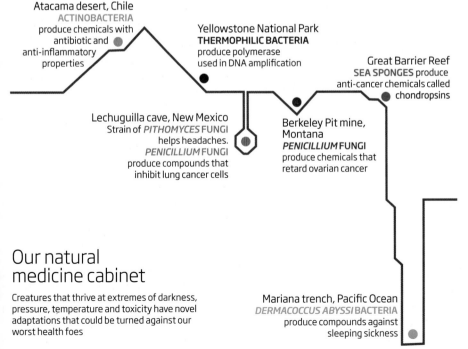

Our natural medicine cabinet

Creatures that thrive at extremes of darkness, pressure, temperature and toxicity have novel adaptations that could be turned against our worst health foes

Atacama desert, Chile
ACTINOBACTERIA
produce chemicals with antibiotic and anti-inflammatory properties

Yellowstone National Park
THERMOPHILIC BACTERIA
produce polymerase used in DNA amplification

Great Barrier Reef
SEA SPONGES produce anti-cancer chemicals called chondropsins

Lechuguilla cave, New Mexico
Strain of *PITHOMYCES* FUNGI helps headaches.
PENICILLIUM FUNGI produce compounds that inhibit lung cancer cells

Berkeley Pit mine, Montana
PENICILLIUM FUNGI produce chemicals that retard ovarian cancer

Mariana trench, Pacific Ocean
DERMACOCCUS ABYSSI BACTERIA produce compounds against sleeping sickness

Field of dreams

The vision of getting plants to make drugs is finally becoming reality, but not in the way most people expected, discovers Hal Hodson

"MY BACKGROUND is that I'm a dentist," says Julian Ma. In the late 1980s, though, he helped to invent something with the potential to put many dentists out of business: a way of eliminating the bacteria that cause cavities, while leaving the rest of the mouth's flora alone. So why do we still live in fear of the dentist's drill?

Ma's antidote to tooth decay consists of antibodies that stop the harmful bacteria sticking to our teeth. But antibodies can be made only by living cells. Without a way to mass produce antibodies cheaply, his antidote was a non-starter. Back in 1990, however, just as Ma finished his doctorate, a solution seemed to present itself. A team in California managed to get a plant to produce antibodies. Ma made a call and soon he was on a plane to California. "That was serendipity, but it came out of a need to start producing something that would be used like toothpaste by millions, billions of people," Ma says.

He found himself participating in the birth of a new science: pharmaceutical farming, or "pharming". It began with big dreams. The flagship hope was the edible vaccine, which was meant to save millions of lives in poor countries by making inoculation as simple as eating fruit.

By making sophisticated medicines dirt cheap, pharming was going to open new doors. "How about, even, like, washing yourself in an antibody against *Staph aureus*?" Ma suggests. "You can start to wonder about where you could use antibodies in new situations. They could replace antibiotics completely."

We are not there yet. But the pharming revolution is finally getting under way. The first plant-produced protein drug was approved in the US in 2012, and many more are in the pipeline. The revolution is not happening in quite in the way the pioneers envisaged, though.

Part of the reason why pharming has been so slow to take off is technological. Lots of medicines are already extracted from plants, of course, but these are usually small molecules naturally produced in large quantities. Getting plants to make foreign proteins such as antibodies requires genetic

"Antibodies can only be made by living cells, and we need a way to mass produce them cheaply"

engineering, which is a slow, hit-and-miss process. First you have to add the required genes to cells, then grow plants from them, which takes months.

At this stage, you might discover that none of the plants produce enough of the desired protein, or that the protein does not have the desired effect. Even if all goes well, you still have to generate true-breeding lines for large-scale production. "This can often take several years," says George Lomonossoff at the John Innes Centre in Norwich, UK.

Because of these issues, many of the first would-be pharmers chose to engineer food plants such as maize, even though they were not aiming to create edible products. Food plants are much easier to work with because there is so much knowledge and experience to draw on. This decision, though, made it harder to get permission to grow the modified plants in open fields. Members of the public were understandably nervous about their food being contaminated, and many scientists agreed that only non-food crops should be used to produce drugs.

In the US, this issue came to a head in 2002. The previous year, in a field in Nebraska, a farmer had grown corn modified to produce an unnamed substance for a company ➤

Shortcut to growing drugs

Growing pharmaceutical products in crops used to require genetically engineering plants, which can take years. Now products can be produced in just weeks using transient gene expression

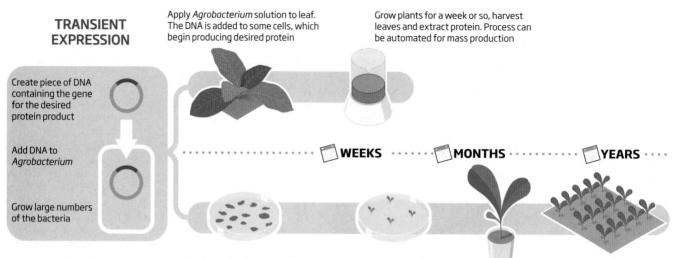

TRANSIENT EXPRESSION

Apply *Agrobacterium* solution to leaf. The DNA is added to some cells, which begin producing desired protein

Grow plants for a week or so, harvest leaves and extract protein. Process can be automated for mass production

Create piece of DNA containing the gene for the desired protein product

Add DNA to *Agrobacterium*

Grow large numbers of the bacteria

WEEKS ···· MONTHS ···· YEARS ····

GENETIC MODIFICATION

Apply *Agrobacterium* solution to pieces of a plant. The bacteria adds desired DNA to some cells

Regenerate entire plants from the few cells that incorporated the added DNA into their genomes

Create true-breeding plants and generate enough seeds for commercial production

---

called ProdiGene. In 2002, when the farmer planted soya beans for food production, leftover maize seeds sprouted and were discovered growing among the soya. The resulting controversy had major repercussions. It led to an abrupt end to ProdiGene's projects and a tightening of the rules for growing pharma crops in the open. Many companies abandoned the idea of pharming in open fields altogether.

Getting permission to pharm outdoors is relatively easy compared with the next stage, though: carrying out clinical trials to prove that a product is safe and effective. Drug approval is a slow and very expensive process, and it is even more difficult when the drug in question has been produced in a new way.

One worry, for instance, is that a protein produced in a plant cell is not necessarily the same as an animal version with an identical sequence. Cells tack sugars onto proteins, and plant cells don't always add the same sugars as animal cells. This means some plant-grown proteins can trigger an immune reaction if they are injected into a person's bloodstream. To get around the issue, some groups are modifying plants to add the same sugars as animals, but this will take time.

With so many hurdles, it is hardly surprising that progress has been so slow. Ma, now at St George's, University of London, did manage to create a tobacco plant capable of producing his tooth-decay antibodies, but more than 20 years later, the commercial version of the technology – CaroRx – has yet to be launched despite successful small trials. In fact, only one plant-grown drug has so far been given the green light from the US Food and Drug

Administration (FDA), although a few plant-grown products are being used commercially.

One is being made in Cuba, whose Centre for Genetic Engineering and Biotechnology in Havana created a pioneering vaccine against hepatitis B, Heberbiovac-HB, which has been exported to more than 30 other countries. The active ingredient is purified using an antibody, which used to be made by immunising mice against hepatitis B and extracting the antibody-producing cells.

In 2006, the centre started using a plant-made antibody to purify the hepatitis vaccine. The "plantibody" is extracted from modified tobacco plants grown in an indoor, soil-free system. The advance has reportedly reduced costs and boosted production of the vaccine –

> **"The conventionally made drug is one of the most expensive ever, costing $200,000 a year"**

and spared the lives of thousands of mice.

Another pioneer is Ventria Bioscience of Fort Collins, Colorado, which is growing rice that produces proteins such as lactoferrin, found in milk, tears and saliva. It helps protect against infections and, unlike most pharm products, it is already common in most people's diets. That means there should be no risk even if contamination occurred. Even so, Ventria is allowed to grow its rice only in sites far from normal rice fields. The company produces human lactoferrin for adding to formula milk for infants. It also hopes to get

its lactoferrin approved as a treatment for preventing diarrhoea in vulnerable patients put on antibiotics. It is, however, just about the only company pharming in open fields.

Most other groups are taking a different approach, largely thanks to advances in technology. One is the development of ways of growing plant cells, rather than whole plants, in big vats, in a similar way to production using animal cells. Large quantities of cells can be grown faster than entire plants. The big advantage of using plant cells rather than animal cells is that there is no risk of infection by mammalian viruses that could infect people too.

And because the cells are grown in sealed chambers and no seeds or pollen are ever produced, there is no risk of the added genes getting into any agricultural or wild strain of plant. This means companies do not need the kind of approval required to grow genetically modified plants in open fields.

"We have the best of both worlds," says David Aviezer, then head of Protalix Biotherapeutics in Carmiel, Israel, the leading company in this field. "Because we use cells, not field-grown plants, we don't come under the same rules." Using plant cell cultures is more about ensuring that the end product is pure than about preventing genetically modified material contaminating the environment or the food chain, he says, but it achieves both.

The company's first product is a treatment for Gaucher disease, a rare genetic condition in which an enzyme deficiency causes a fatty build-up in vital organs. Protalix is producing a synthetic version of this enzyme, called taliglucerase alfa, in modified carrot cells grown in huge, disposable plastic sacks. The only thing carrot-like about the process is the colour of the culture (pictured, below). In May 2012, taliglucerase alfa became the first genetically engineered protein produced by plants to receive full FDA approval.

The plant-grown enzyme will be competing with another version of the missing enzyme, called imiglucerase, which is produced using vats of Chinese hamster ovary cells by a firm called Genzyme at a factory in Allston, Massachusetts. It is one of the most expensive drugs ever, costing $200,000 per patient per year – and it needs to be taken for life. Worse still, Genzyme had to temporarily shut down production in 2009 because of viral contamination, leading to shortages.

The prospect of producing drugs more cheaply and safely in vats of plant cells has got big pharma interested. Drug giant Pfizer has licensed Protalix's technology, so taliglucerase alfa could be the first of many drugs grown this way. It is still a far cry from the dream of producing drugs very cheaply, though. At something like $150,000 a year, taliglucerase alfa will be cheaper, but it could hardly be described as cheap.

A shortcut to making proteins in plants could help bring that vision closer. Instead of spending months or years creating genetically engineered plants, the idea is to add DNA coding for the desired protein to the leaves of normal plants. This is usually done by infiltrating the leaves of tobacco plants with a solution containing a bacterium called *Agrobacterium*, which can get pieces of DNA inside plant cells. Then all you have to do is wait a week or two for the leaves to produce the protein and harvest the leaves. This method is known as transient expression, because protein production would gradually stop after a few weeks (see diagram, left). The added DNA rarely gets incorporated into the genomes of cells and instead slowly breaks down.

Although transient expression offers an enormous advantage in terms of speed, it has never been practical commercially because very little protein is produced. Researchers have tried all kinds of tricks to boost protein expression, such as introducing RNAs that replicate themselves in a similar manner to viruses, with little success.

This is where Lomonossoff comes in. He discovered that a plant virus, the cowpea mosaic virus, has sequences flanking its genes that hugely increase protein expression. Add another sequence that disables a plant's in-built defences against foreign RNA and it is possible to get more than a gram of the desired protein per kilogram of plant weight – which is a lot.

His team's "hyper translatable" system can be used on a small scale to speed up research, by producing a few milligrams of a protein at a time. It is also being scaled up for producing kilograms by companies such as Medicago of Quebec, Canada. It has sealed greenhouses full of tobacco plants, and has developed an automated system for infiltrating these plants with the desired DNA. It is using the technology to make flu vaccines. Its vaccines consist of an empty shell – a virus-like particle – embedded with the surface proteins of the relevant flu virus.

Flu vaccines are normally produced using chicken eggs, and with eggs it takes several months to produce a vaccine to a new flu virus. Medicago has proved that it can do it just three weeks after getting the sequence of the new virus. "We download a flu's genetic sequence from the internet and use it to make a DNA fragment which we clone into *Agrobacterium*," says Andy Sheldon, head of Medicago.

Running the numbers

Medicago has received funding from the US military to develop and test ways of producing vaccines rapidly in case of, say, a flu pandemic. It has built a facility in North Carolina capable of producing 10 million doses a month. Sheldon claims the plant-based method is not only faster, but 10 to 20 times cheaper than conventional ways of making flu vaccines, so it might one day be used for producing normal seasonal flu vaccines – and perhaps many other kinds of proteins, too. Medicago has "run the numbers" on the production of antibodies, and Sheldon thinks greenhouse production would be cost effective. So is there any need for pharming in open fields at all?

Yes, says Ma. He has been leading a project, run by the Pharma-Planta research consortium, to produce anti-HIV antibodies in tobacco, one of which successfully passed a clinical trial. Only open-field growing would allow a cocktail of antibodies to be produced cheaply enough to combat HIV in sub-Saharan Africa, he says. Building greenhouses is too expensive. The same is true for non-pharmaceutical products such as industrial enzymes, which usually need to be dirt cheap to compete in the market.

For high-value products for rich countries, though, sealed greenhouses could be the way forward. "Greenhouse technology is amazing now," says Ma. "In Holland or southern Spain they look like cities, they're huge."

So pharming is finally becoming a reality, but it looks as though it will mostly take place behind closed doors rather than in open fields. Unfortunately, if the price tag for taliglucerase alfa is anything to go by, it may be a few years yet before we start washing with antibodies or brushing our teeth with them. ∎

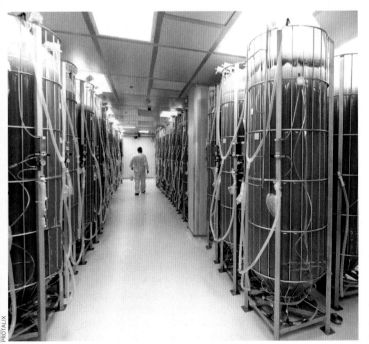

The clue's in the colour – these are vats of carrot cells

Does the urgency to treat breast cancer at the earliest stage possible mean some women are having unnecessary surgery, asks **Tiffany O'Callaghan**

The cruellest cut?

PLAINPICTURE

T HE lump in her right breast was smaller than a pea. When she first noticed it, in August 2011, 28-year-old photographer Ellen Doherty was busy working on an exhibition. She put off visiting the doctor for a month.

When Doherty finally went, the doctor said it was probably nothing to worry about. But they did a scan to be sure – and that led to several more tests. Finally they said she had a 2.8-millimetre tumour known as ductal carcinoma in situ, or DCIS.

Like many women given this diagnosis, Doherty had never heard of it before. She quickly devoured any information she could find, but came away confused.

The term "in situ" means that the cancerous cells are contained within the breast's milk ducts and have not invaded the surrounding tissue. This kind of lesion is not harmful unless it progresses past that stage and becomes invasive, but it is treated just as aggressively as invasive cancer. Yet this approach is increasingly being questioned

as evidence emerges that for some women DCIS would not turn out to be dangerous.

In fact, DCIS could be regarded as a creation of modern medicine, as most cases are found through breast screening – 30 years ago it was rarely diagnosed. The fear is that screening may be leading us to cut out lumps that, left alone, would have never caused a problem. "Are we helping people by diagnosing it, or are we making things worse?" asks Beth Virnig, who monitors cancer surveillance and detection data at the University of

Minnesota in Minneapolis. Breast cancer used to be discovered only if it formed a noticeable lump or caused other symptoms such as nipple discharge. Since the advent of breast screening programmes in the 1980s, using X-rays known as mammograms, it is more commonly found that way. And that means growing numbers of DCIS cases are being detected. In the US, the incidence has grown more than eightfold since the 1980s (see graph, right). DCIS now makes up about a quarter of breast cancer cases found through screening.

When a mammogram turns up an abnormality, the next step is a biopsy to remove a small sample of the tissue in question. If the diagnosis is DCIS, the options are the same as for invasive cancer: excision of a lump containing the growth, if possible, or removal of the breast. To Doherty this seemed bizarre: "How can they cut one of your boobs off for something that's not going to kill you?"

Doherty had a lumpectomy in November 2011, but while she was recovering, a doctor called to say the affected tissue was more widespread than they thought and they hadn't cut out enough. The following January she had a mastectomy.

This zero-tolerance approach to DCIS is based on the assumption that, given the chance, it will progress to invasive cancer. Yet no one knows how often that assumption is correct.

Disappearing tumours

It may sound surprising, but people can have small cancers that do them no harm; autopsies can reveal "incidental cancers" that were not the cause of death. Some tumours are so slow-growing that they never cause a problem, whereas others, including some cases of breast cancer, go away on their own, presumably eliminated by the immune system.

Scour the medical literature for a figure for how often DCIS progresses to invasive cancer if left untreated and you will find estimates as low as 14 per cent and as high as 75 per cent, a range so broad as to be almost meaningless. There has never been a large study of women given this diagnosis who don't have surgery, so the progression rate can only be inferred by indirect means.

Take, for instance, a study of laboratory tissue samples from women who had a breast lump biopsied many decades ago, and went untreated because tests at the time indicated it was benign. Re-examining those biopsies turned up some in which a mistake had been

made and the woman actually had DCIS. Of 71 such cases where they could track down the women, about half had gone on to develop invasive breast cancer.

That figure is probably an overestimate, though, because the women in that study had DCIS that had grown big enough to be felt as a lump. "Mammographically detected DCIS has a much lower risk of invasive cancer than DCIS detected [as a lump]," says Karla Kerlikowske, an epidemiologist at the University of California, San Francisco (UCSF).

There is another kind of evidence that suggests our current approach might be wrong. If this condition usually progresses to invasive cancer, then catching and cutting out more cases of DCIS should lead to a drop in cases of invasive cancer. That is what has happened with colon cancer: the removal of small precancerous growths, or polyps, in the colon detected through screening by colonoscopy has coincided with falling rates of colon cancer (see graph, right).

This isn't happening with breast cancer, which suggests one of two things: either the rate of invasive breast cancer is rising, or most cases of DCIS would not go on to become invasive cancer. While DCIS incidence rates have steadily climbed over the past 30 years, the figures for invasive breast cancer dipped only slightly in the mid 2000s. Because of the timing this is largely attributed to fewer women using hormone replacement therapy, which can stimulate tumour growth. "Not until the decrease in hormone therapy did we see a decline in invasive cancer," says Kerlikowske. "If DCIS was a true precursor, one would expect a decline in invasive cancer much sooner."

If we are indeed going wrong with our treatment of DCIS, what are the alternatives? About three-quarters of breast cancers are fuelled by the female reproductive hormone oestrogen, and drugs that block this hormone are already used alongside surgery. Could they be used instead of surgery?

In a study published in 2011, 14 women whose DCIS was oestrogen-sensitive chose to forgo surgery and received drug treatment alone. Eight nevertheless ended up having surgery, and five of these women were found to have had progression to invasive cancer. The other six carried on without surgery, and two stopped the drugs. After up to seven years of follow-up, none of the non-surgery six had any signs of invasive breast cancer. "What we really want to do is identify the women who are stable without any intervention – or are ➤

Cancer mystery

If detecting breast cancer early prevents it from spreading, why has there been no decline in invasive breast cancer rates since screening programmes started in the 1980s?

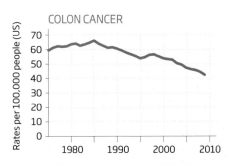

COLON CANCER

The incidence of colon cancer has fallen since the introduction of screening and removal of the polyps thought to lead to cancer

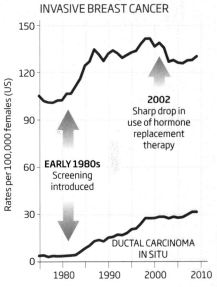

INVASIVE BREAST CANCER

2002
Sharp drop in use of hormone replacement therapy

EARLY 1980s
Screening introduced

DUCTAL CARCINOMA IN SITU

SOURCE: US NATIONAL CANCER INSTITUTE

Breast cancer screening led to a rise in cases of ductal carcinoma in situ, seen as an early form of cancer and removed surgically. But rates of invasive breast cancer have not fallen as a result

"Some tumours grow so slowly that they never cause a problem, while others may be dealt with by the immune system"

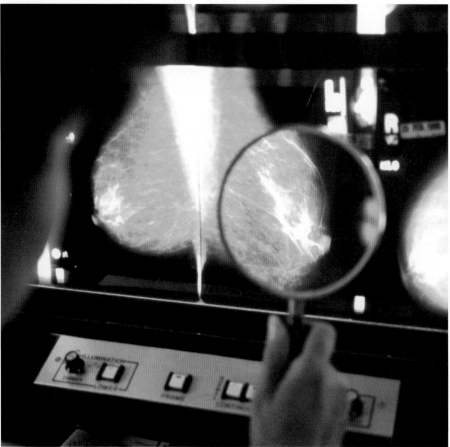

Mammograms
revolutionised breast
cancer diagnosis

carcinoma, which most people are aware is synonymous with cancer. "The fear attached to the word 'cancer' leads people to overreact and makes it hard to develop more prudent and cautious approaches," says H. Gilbert Welch of Dartmouth College in New Hampshire, who studies overdiagnosis in cancer screening.

Not all agree. According to the grading system applied to all tumours, DCIS is currently classed as stage 0, and Van Zee believes this already makes it clear it is different to invasive breast cancer. The emotional impact of this issue is clear in online forums. One woman with DCIS who had a lumpectomy, mastectomy and radiotherapy summed it up: "Don't tell me I didn't have cancer."

Sense of urgency

With or without a name change, it would help if healthcare systems were better geared up to distinguish between DCIS and invasive cancer. UK guidelines, for instance, say that all cancer patients should be treated within one month of diagnosis, and that sense of urgency can put undue pressure on women still grappling with a confusing diagnosis. "With DCIS, women don't need to jump to make a decision," says Joann Elmore, an epidemiologist at the University of Washington in Seattle. "You don't need to have a mastectomy tomorrow."

One day we may be able to make better informed decisions using cancer biomarkers – testing the molecular make-up of biopsied DCIS tissue to see which are most likely to progress to invasive cancer. Kerlikowske has found that people whose tissue was positive for three proteins, COX-2, p16 and Ki67, had nearly a 20 per cent risk of developing invasive cancer after surgery to remove the lesion, while those who were triple negative had just over a 4 per cent risk.

While efforts continue to better distinguish the deceptive from the deadly, women with DCIS are still left with uncertainty. On the day Doherty was scheduled for surgery it was an act of considerable will to show up at the hospital. Had it been an option, she would gladly have taken part in a trial investigating alternatives. Without that chance, she was grateful to a nurse for her candour. "She didn't make any attempt to bluff," Doherty says. The nurse told her: "It's shit – we don't know what it is."

Doherty was left stunned by her experience. "The uncertainty is an eye-opener," she says. "However advanced we are as a society, there is so much we still don't know about the human body." ∎

stable with hormone therapy alone," says Shelley Hwang, a breast cancer specialist at Duke University Hospital in Durham, North Carolina, who led that study.

Could we go a step further? It is becoming more common for men diagnosed with prostate cancer to be offered the option of "watchful waiting" instead of surgery, getting regular blood tests and biopsies to monitor signs of progression. Some breast surgeons are starting to wonder if this might also be an option for women with low-grade DCIS, where the cells still look similar to normal duct cells.

Laura Esserman, a breast cancer specialist at UCSF, believes change will be driven by patients. She points out that until the 1970s, the standard response to breast cancer was a painful and debilitating "radical mastectomy", removing the entire breast, underlying chest muscle and nearby lymph nodes. Now that is rarely done. "The reason we don't do radical mastectomies any more is because of the courage that patients had to want to come up with something else," she says. It is something their doctors can learn from, she adds.

Breast cancer surgeon Adele Francis at University Hospital Birmingham in the UK may have what it takes. She has started recruiting women with low-grade DCIS to a five-year trial that will compare surgery with monitoring through annual mammograms. Like Esserman, Francis believes it will take determined patients to chart the way. "To take part in any sort of clinical trial once you've had a diagnosis like this, it takes courage," she says.

It's a hard decision to make while the current approach of surgery for all still has many defenders. "While [DCIS] may be 'overtreated', early detection and treatment saves lives," says Kimberly Van Zee, a breast cancer specialist at the Memorial Sloan-Kettering Cancer Center in New York City. Yet Francis says about 80 per cent of the 54 colleagues she contacted about the trial were keen to take part. "The only way that this uncertainty can be addressed is by treating patients within trials," she says.

As well as changing the way we treat DCIS, there may be other ways to improve matters. One recommendation of a 2009 conference on DCIS held by the US National Institutes of Health was to do away with the term

> "The fear attached to the word 'cancer' leads people to overreact and makes it hard to develop more cautious approaches"

Receive £25k tax-free to retrain as a chemistry teacher and spark a lifelong interest in chemistry.

Switching to a career as a chemistry teacher is a lot more achievable than you might think. You could receive a £25k* tax-free bursary or a £25k* scholarship provided by the Royal Society of Chemistry, as well as support and advice from our Premier Plus service. Alternatively, you could earn a salary while you train. Then you get to inspire young people with the subject you love.

Apply now.
Visit education.gov.uk/teachchemistry

ROYAL SOCIETY OF **CHEMISTRY**

TEACHING
YOUR FUTURE | THEIR FUTURE

Department for Education

*Conditions apply. Visit education.gov.uk/teachconditions

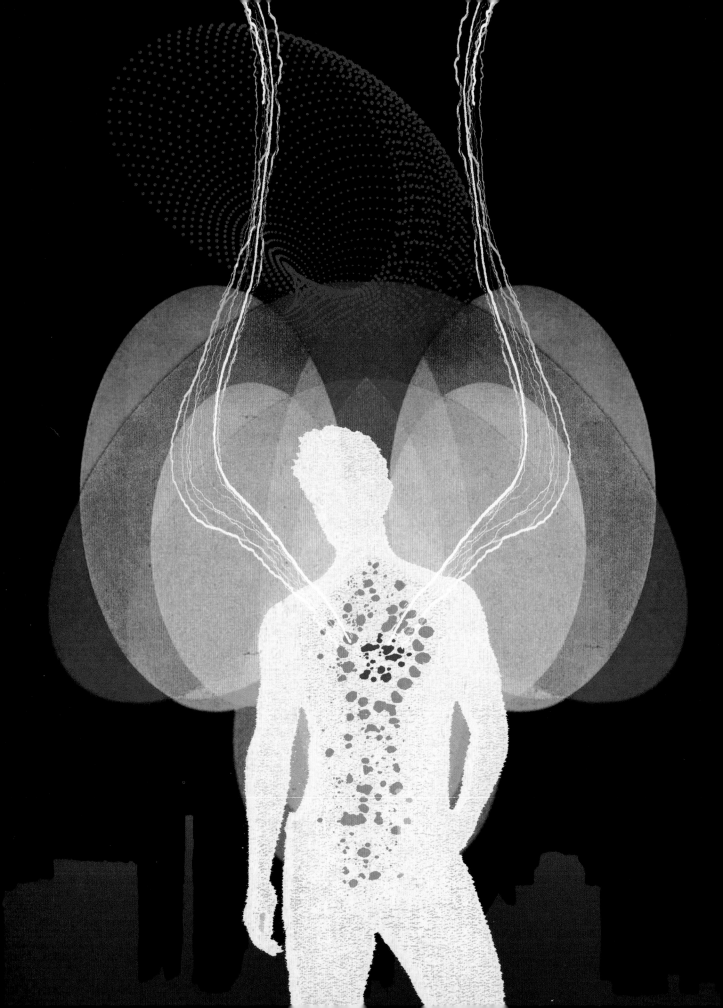

T IS the medical symptom that many of us fear the most: a lump. If it turns out to be cancer, we face, at best, a painful and debilitating course of treatment, and at worst, well... the worst.

And yet, paradoxically, this lump is not what kills most people. As long as it is somewhere accessible, a single, discrete tumour can usually be cut out.

It is only once cells escape from this primary tumour and settle elsewhere in the body – like the brain, liver, lungs or bones – that cancer typically becomes deadly. At this stage, there may be so many secondary tumours that repeated surgery becomes a losing battle.

This spreading process, called metastasis, is what kills 9 out of 10 people who die from cancer. "Metastasis is one of the most important problems in the treatment of cancer," says Chris Marshall, who studies the phenomenon at the Institute of Cancer Research in London.

Despite its importance, the way cancers spread has for a long time remained opaque. But things are changing. New techniques to study metastasis have led to the alarming finding that standard medical procedures to investigate and treat cancer can sometimes help it spread.

Armed with this knowledge of how cancer disperses, however, researchers are devising ways to trap and snare cancer cells as they head off on this journey. As a result a whole new front is opening up in the war on cancer.

The idea that cancer spreads from its initial site to take root in other parts of the body was first described in 1829 by a French gynaecologist called Joseph Récamier, who coined the term "metastasis". Yet it has taken a remarkably long time to understand this process. That's largely because the usual ways we investigate disease have failed us. In people, there was no good way to monitor cells escaping from a primary tumour and travelling around the body in real time. We can count secondary tumours only once they are established and large enough to show up on a scan. In mice, the go-to model for most diseases, it is rare for cancer to metastasise naturally.

On the move

Nevertheless, slow progress has been made. Improvements in scanning and imaging technology mean we can discern ever-smaller secondary tumours in the human body. And by the 1990s, genetically engineered mice were being created that were predisposed to developing tumours that spread. It is now even possible to implant a glass porthole into the abdomen of such mice and watch fluorescent tumour cells in motion.

From these advances, we now know that metastasis is a remarkable process, requiring cancer cells to perform a series of distinct feats. First they must stop dividing and acquire the ability to change shape, enabling them to squeeze their way, like an amoeba or slug, into surrounding tissue. If these errant cells break into a blood vessel – or lymph vessel, a waste-collection system that drains into the blood – they will be swept into the torrent that is our circulation. Here many tumour cells will succumb to physical damage, or attack from patrolling immune cells. "The bloodstream is an ugly, mean place," says Kenneth Pienta, an oncologist at the Johns Hopkins Hospital in Baltimore, Maryland. "For a cancer cell to go through the heart would be like us going over Niagara Falls without a barrel."

Any tumour cells that survive this ordeal must still manage to stick to the blood vessel wall at a new site, wiggle through it into the surrounding tissue, and start dividing once more. Put this way, it's a wonder that any secondary tumours form at all. But only one tumour cell need survive this journey for cancer to spread. So many researchers are now looking for ways to intercept these marauding tumour cells.

That goal is more pressing than ever. The development of ways to monitor levels of migrating tumour cells in the blood (see "Liquid biopsy", page 60) has prompted ➤

FATAL ATTRACTION

Traps and lures could stop cancer from spreading around the body, boosting chances of survival. **Clare Wilson** reports

JIMMY TURRELL

LIQUID BIOPSY

Most deaths from cancer happen after cells have escaped from a primary tumour and set up house elsewhere in the body (see main story). But it is only in the past decade that we have developed tools to track this process.

A test called CellSearch allows doctors to count how many cancer cells are in a teaspoon of blood. A reading of five or more cancer cells suggests that the tumour is spreading.

One use of the test is to help give people a realistic prognosis. While cancer is often portrayed as a disease that should be fought to the death, some people choose not to spend their last months undergoing harsh treatments if there is little hope of cure.

But counting tumour cells in the blood can also help to keep people alive. Repeating the test over time reveals whether the primary tumour is responding to drug therapy. If the count keeps rising, that tells doctors they need to switch treatments.

The test has its limitations, though. At below five cells in the sample, the accuracy suffers: some people who do have secondary tumours score zero, because no cells end up in the sample.

Another idea is to scour the patient's entire blood supply for cancerous cells much like kidney dialysis, in which people whose kidneys are failing have their blood removed, filtered and then returned.

In the case of cancer, the removed blood would be passed through a column containing antibodies that bind to the cancer cells and trap them as they pass. Drugs can then be tested on the extracted cancer cells, to see which would be most effective.

"It gives us the opportunity to collect tumour cells without sticking a needle into a metastasis," says Gerhardt Attard of the Institute of Cancer Research in London, who is part of a consortium developing the technique.

This will be disturbing knowledge for anyone who has to undergo cancer surgery. Yet it is still better to cut the tumour out and risk it spreading than to leave it alone to develop this ability by itself. And on the positive side, says Zharov, the most promising new ways to block metastasis might be most efficiently deployed while biopsies or surgery are in progress.

Perhaps the most obvious approach is to develop drugs that block some molecular pathway vital to cancer cells in the process of metastasising. One target is the crawling-around stage, one of cancer cells' more unusual abilities.

Marshall's team is investigating a group of enzymes called rho kinases that help pull cancer cells into the different shapes they need to crawl through tissues. "We would really like to develop a preventative," says Marshall. "You take a dose every day and it would reduce the chance of metastasis."

There are other, more creative approaches in the works, including physical traps loaded with chemicals that are irresistible to roaming cancer cells. The nature of this chemical lure would depend on the type of cancer. Prostate and breast tumour cells, for instance, are attracted to a molecule called SDF-1, present in bone marrow. That is why both of these types of cancer often spread to the skeleton, says Pienta.

His team has found that a tiny, soft sponge loaded with SDF-1 can attract tumour cells if placed underneath the skin of mice with a

a worrying discovery: some of the things we do to diagnose and treat cancer can inadvertently send tumour cells surging into the blood.

The suspect procedures include biopsies – in which a small piece of the tumour is removed with a needle – and even surgery to remove a tumour. "Surgery is a severe problem. It might produce millions of tumour cells, increasing the risk of metastasis," says Vladimir Zharov, who heads the Arkansas Nanomedicine Center in Little Rock.

This is such a recent finding that it is unclear exactly how it happens, says Zharov, who was one of the first to witness such surges. In some patients a distinct spike of tumour cells in the blood can be measured during tumour-removal operations, so it could be that surgeons are unintentionally cutting into the tumour. Or perhaps just cutting into a tumour's blood supply creates suction, pulling tumour cells into the surrounding blood vessels, he speculates.

The cancer trap

Most cancers only become deadly once cells break free from the primary tumour and spread around the body. Catching and eradicating these migrating cells should increase a person's chances of survival

Abnormal cells start to grow and multiply

Injected **magnetic nanoparticles** coated with antibodies attach to cancer cells

A magnet on the hand causes the **nanoparticles** and cancer cells to collect in one place, near the skin

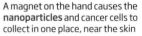

LASER

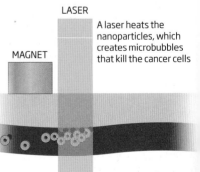

A laser heats the nanoparticles, which creates microbubbles that kill the cancer cells

MAGNET

Some **cancer cells** can change shape and push through tissue

Surgery and biopsies can cause **tumour cells** to surge into the bloodstream

"The shock of being ejected into the blood might be enough to kill most of the tumour cells"

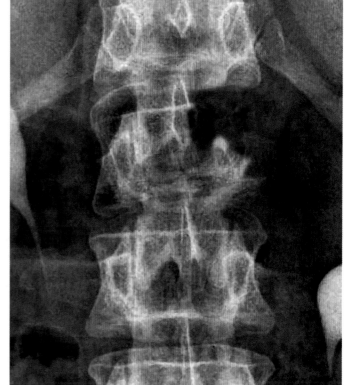

CAVALLINI JAMES/BSIP/SCIENCE PHOTO LIBRARY

version of prostate cancer. Pienta suspects, however, that if this were done in cancer patients, not enough cancer cells would be caught to prevent metastases. So before they move to trials in people, his team is developing materials that could sit right inside a blood vessel without impeding blood flow.

Other cancers may be easier to snare, though. Rather than travelling through the bloodstream, ovarian cancer cells tend to escape into the peritoneal cavity inside the abdomen and latch on to organs such as the colon and bladder. So a device called M-trap has been designed to sit in the abdomen and chemically lure in wandering cancer cells.

Although the results have yet to be published, mice with ovarian cancer that had the trap implanted lived significantly longer than those given no treatment, says Miguel Abal at the Santiago University Hospital Complex in Spain, who invented the device.

In people, the idea is to implant the trap during surgery to remove the primary tumour, and replace the trap periodically. Women with ovarian cancer often have microscopic secondary tumours which cause the disease to return after each surgery. Abal hopes the M-trap would mop up enough of the metastasising cells to tip the balance in favour of long-term recovery.

Still, putting traps inside the body is an invasive approach, and some people with cancer are too weak to withstand repeated operations. An arguably more elegant solution is to intercept roving cancer cells without surgical intervention, using magnets, an approach being pioneered by Zharov's team.

The first step is to make any circulating tumour cells magnetic, by attaching cancer-specific antibodies to magnetic nanoparticles and injecting them into the blood. The antibodies home in on tumour cells and bind to them. Simply holding a magnet over the skin causes the cancer cells in the blood to collect at that spot. These cells can then be killed using a laser that penetrates the skin. It heats up the nanoparticles, triggering the formation of tiny bubbles around them that destroy the cancer cells (see diagram, left). This technique has already been shown to work in mice (see also "Surgery's new sound", page 86).

The big question is whether such an approach can be scaled up to work in people. In mice, turning the laser up too high burned their skin, but there was a middle ground where cancer cells were killed without damaging healthy tissue.

The technology has now been licensed to

Don't get comfy: Secondary tumours in bone could be evicted

San Francisco biotechnology firm Accurexa, which aims to run clinical trials in women having surgery for breast cancer. The idea is to round up and kill those tumour cells that might surge into the blood during the operation.

Just before surgery, each woman will have a magnet attached over her palm and be injected with the nanoparticles. An hour after the surgery is finished, any circulating tumour cells should have gathered at the woman's palm, where they will be zapped by the laser.

Longer-term use, such as in people whose primary tumours are inoperable, might involve wearing such a magnet permanently and receiving nanoparticle injections and laser therapy, perhaps twice a week. Zharov doubts that this could completely prevent secondary tumours. "But we might at least slow the process down," he says.

Forced eviction

There is a problem, though. While these novel methods of intercepting cancer cells as they journey from primary tumour to secondary sites may seem promising, many people are only diagnosed with cancer once it has already spread.

There may be ways to intervene at this stage, says Pienta. He believes it might be possible to reverse the process of metastasis after new tumours have formed. It's a radical idea, but work in mice suggests that disrupting the crosstalk between cells of secondary tumours and their environment can cause the tumour

cells to be evicted and dumped back into the blood again, where they might be dealt with more easily.

Pienta is exploring this idea with prostate and breast cancers. Their affinity for the bone-marrow chemical SDF-1 seems to arise because the cancer cells mimic healthy, blood-forming stem cells – whose normal home is within our bones. By good fortune, a drug already exists that blocks cells binding to SDF-1, which is given to people with blood cancer to flush blood stem cells out of their bone marrow.

When mice with prostate cancer receive injections of this drug, the cells of their secondary tumours are ejected from the bones into the bloodstream. This raises the tantalising possibility that the same approach could be used to help people with breast or prostate cancer that has spread to their bones.

Pienta thinks that the shock of being ejected into the blood might be enough to kill most of the tumour cells. But if not, giving the patient a short blast of intense chemotherapy at the same time should finish the job. His team hopes to carry out a trial in men with prostate cancer.

None of these techniques is likely to put a complete halt to cancer spreading, at least in their current incarnations. Yet just being able to slow or reduce the process could add years to people's lives. And it has only become possible thanks to our slow unravelling of the mysteries of metastasis, says Marshall. "It's giving us a window of opportunity." ∎

What's really going on in those cancer cells?

Forty years after President Nixon's war on cancer sanctioned billions of research dollars, progress is still glacial. But radical approaches shaped by physics rather than biology could change everything, says **Paul Davies**

A cultured breast cancer cell starts to migrate outwards

Burgeoning health costs are a major issue in the US. High on the list of those costs is cancer therapy, with the clamour for hugely expensive drugs – many of which have little or no clinical benefit – set to grow as baby boomers age.

Cancer research swallows billions of dollars a year, but the life expectancy for someone diagnosed with cancer that has spread to other parts of the body has changed little over several decades. Therapy is often a haphazard rearguard action against the inevitable. And the search for a general cure remains as elusive as ever.

Recognising this depressing impasse, the US National Cancer Institute (NCI) took a bold step in 2008 by deciding that the field might benefit from the input of mathematicians and physical scientists,

"Like ageing, cancer is not so much a disease as a process"

whose methods and insights differ markedly from those of cancer biologists.

After all, the history of science teaches us that major advances come when a subject's conceptual foundations are revised. Maybe progress is slow because we are looking at the problem in the wrong way? So the NCI created 12 centres for physical science and oncology. They are now starting to bear fruit, for example, by showing how the elastic properties of cells change as cancer progresses.

In the 19th century, living organisms were widely regarded as machines infused by vital forces. Biologists eventually came to realise that cells are not some sort of magic matter,

but complex networks of chemical reaction pathways. Then came the genetics revolution, which describes life in the informational language of instructions, codes and signalling. Mainstream research today focuses almost exclusively on chemical pathways or genetic sequencing. For example, drugs are designed to block reaction pathways implicated in cancer. The cancer genome atlas is amassing terabytes of data in which people hope to spot some sort of mutational pattern. But while of great scientific interest, such projects have not led to the much-anticipated breakthrough.

Why? There are fundamental obstacles: living cells, including cancer cells, are a bottomless pit of complexity, and cancer cells are notoriously heterogeneous. A reductionist approach that seeks to unravel the details of every pathway of every cancer cell type might employ researchers for decades and consume billions of dollars, with little impact clinically. Linear chains of cause and effect rarely work in biology, which is dominated by elaborate networks of interactions such as feedback and control loops.

There is, however, another way of looking at cells. In addition to being bags of chemicals and information processing systems, they are also physical objects, with properties such as size, mass, shape, elasticity, free energy, surface stickiness and electrical potential. Cancer cells contain pumps, levers, pulleys and other paraphernalia familiar to physicists and engineers. Furthermore, many of these properties are known to change systematically as cancer progresses in malignancy.

First, though, we need to get away from the notion of a cure, and think of controlling or managing cancer. Like ageing, cancer is not so much a disease as a process. And just as the

effects of ageing can be mitigated without a full understanding of the process, the same could be true of cancer.

Many accounts misleadingly describe cancer as rogue cells running amok. In fact, once cancer is triggered, it is usually very deterministic in its behaviour. Primary tumours are rarely the cause of death. It is when cancer spreads around the body and colonises other organs that the patient's prospects deteriorate sharply.

This so-called metastasis is a well characterised, if poorly understood, physical process. Cells migrate from the primary tumour to blood vessels, which they enter

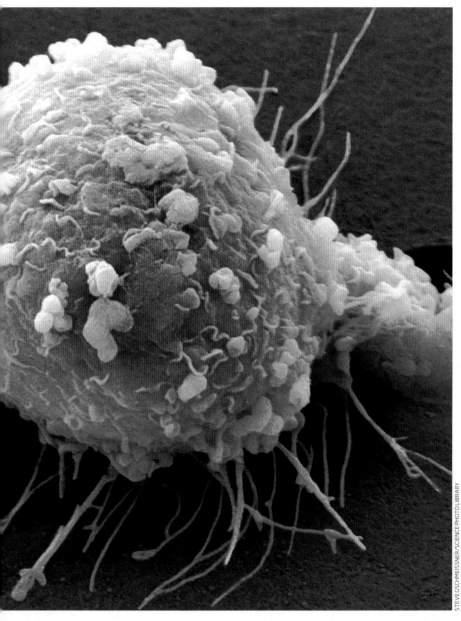
STEVE GSCHMEISSNER/SCIENCE PHOTO LIBRARY

cells in the bone marrow, or as micro-metastases in tissues, before erupting into proliferating secondary tumours. Hence the many cases of "cancer survivors" who die when the same cancer returns with enhanced malignancy years or even decades after a primary tumour has been removed.

The spread of cancer presents many possibilities for clinical intervention once the dream of a cure has been abandoned. For example, if the period of dormancy can be extended by, say, a factor of five, many breast, colon and prostate cancers would cease to be a health issue. How could this be achieved?

Evolutionary roots

We do not need to know the intricate details of the cancer cells' innards to figure out how their overall behaviour might be controlled. It is well known that cells regulate the action of genes not just as a result of chemical signals, but because of the physical properties of their micro-environment. They can sense forces such as shear stresses and the elasticity of nearby tissue. They are also responsive to temperature, electric fields, pH, pressure and oxygen concentration. All these variables offer opportunities for intervening and stabilising widespread cancer cells. For example, a few doctors are attempting to treat cancer using hyperbaric oxygen therapy, where the patient is placed in a chamber of high-pressure pure oxygen, which affects cancer cell metabolism.

We also need to involve other kinds of biologists in cancer research – after all, cancer is widespread among mammals, fish, reptiles, even plants. Clearly it is an integral part of the evolutionary story of multicellular life over the last billion years.

Most normal cells seem to come preloaded with a "cancer subroutine" that can be triggered by a variety of insults, and we need to understand the evolutionary origin of this just as much as the triggering mechanisms. In addition, it has long been recognised that there are many similarities between cancer and embryo development, and evidence is mounting that some genes expressed during embryogenesis get reawakened in cancer.

Right now, the huge cancer research programme is long on technical data, but short on understanding. By reshaping the conceptual landscape, we may at last see how to make serious inroads into tackling a much- feared disease that touches every family on the planet. ∎

through spaces in the vessel walls. Then, swept along in the torrent, they circulate in the blood system, sometimes individually, sometimes "rafting" in gangs like Lilliputian raiders, stuck together by blood platelets. A fraction of these migrants get jammed in tiny blood vessels called venules or, more spectacularly, roll along the vessel wall and fling out little molecular grappling hooks called cadherins. Thus anchored against the blood flow, they inveigle their way into the nearest organ.

During this process, the physical properties and shape of the cells can change dramatically. Generally, cancer cells are soft and misshapen compared with healthy cells of the same

type, a transformation that may affect their motility and increase their invasive potential. Cancer cells are adept at building nests in foreign tissue, by altering the structure and physical properties of the host organ's supporting extracellular matrix, and recruiting local healthy cells. There are also hints that a primary tumour may send out chemical signals ahead of time to prepare the physical and chemical ground for the colonists.

Although metastasis seems fiendishly efficient, most disseminated cancer cells never go on to cause trouble. The vast majority die, and the survivors may lie dormant for years or even decades, either as individual, quiescent,

Print a virus to kill the cancer

It shouldn't take years and a billion dollars to create a new cancer drug. Biohacker **Andrew Hessel** tells **Catherine de Lange** how he aims to do it in a day

You worked in big pharma. Why did you leave?
More than a decade ago, I was with a large biopharma company where I learned first-hand that drug development wasn't really working. Putting tremendous resources into R&D didn't necessarily produce a lot of results, even though we used the most advanced genetic technologies and the best people. I decided to re-evaluate my career, and spent a year on the beach in Thailand thinking about what to do next.

Did inspiration hit you regarding a better way to make drugs?
I had seen technology for printing DNA as far back as 1998 and I thought "this is the answer", because it meant you didn't need to be in a lab to do genetic engineering. You can do the design on computers – something I was very familiar with in bioinformatics – and then print the DNA.

In 2004, I focused on synthetic biology, and in 2009 founded the first cooperative biotech company, Pink Army Cooperative.

It's really about making a specific medicine tailored to one person – "N-of-1" medicine – rather than trying to make it a best fit for a whole population. My vision is to create a personalised treatment that can be made in a day by printing bespoke cancer-fighting viruses. We want to get some of the world's best virologists taking part in the design process, so we have made it open source. It's within reach of any scientist that wants to try it in their own labs.

That's a very ambitious vision, isn't it?
I've never claimed that these technologies will be able to cure anyone first off. The aim is to demonstrate that you can sit at a laptop and design a virus that you believe will infect and kill specific cancer cells, have that virus printed, and test it in culture, all for a few hundred dollars. It is a revolutionary idea for people who think it costs a billion dollars to build a personalised drug... or any drug.

Is that feasible with the state of technology?
In 2012 I joined Autodesk, based in San Rafael, California, which focuses on software design. At that time, the DNA-synthesis firms out there

> ## "I never want to sell a drug. I see the business model as something like Netflix"

could not routinely print even the smallest viral genomes. But by the end of 2013, some of these firms were calling me back saying they could do it. What we're seeing is just the start of being able to make more and more virus particles really inexpensively. So the question now is how do we put together this whole pipeline to design, build and test cancer drugs?

Why focus on cancer-fighting viruses?
For lots of reasons. For me, they are the best examples of inexpensive programmable drugs. And they can hack a cancer cell and turn it into a virus-manufacturing plant, so you only need a very small amount of virus to act as a seed.

The focus also has to be on something we can design and customise easily using software. A virus is not dumb like a chemical, which does one job. A virus has logic mechanisms and switches, so they are very tunable and programmable: in viral engineering, you can actually build combinations of segments of code into your design. We also need to be able to print these viruses using DNA printers, so it's useful that they have only a small amount of DNA. Finally, there is a very long history of oncolytic – cancer-fighting – viruses being used in R&D.

Have such viruses been successfully used?
There were no good anecdotal cases of oncolytic virus use until a few years ago. One of the first I saw was the case of Emily Whitehead, who as a 6-year-old had horrific childhood leukaemia that was treated using an engineered HIV virus (modified so it couldn't cause disease) that reprogrammed her immune cells to fight off her cancer. That was a dramatic success.

And in 2014, the Mayo Clinic published a paper on two people with multiple myeloma. The researchers used a modified measles virus and showed that it perfectly targeted the cancer in both patients. These cancers were resistant to other treatments, and one patient went into full remission after one viral treatment. These types of case are what you'd expect from N-of-1 treatments. They are the beacons for ongoing development.

Once you have the DNA-printing technology up and running, what happens next?
I'm going to build and test this in three stages. Once the technical foundation is in place, we'll take some cancer cells in culture and open up the software for researchers to design a cancer-fighting virus and test it against those cells. Step two is doing this in cats and dogs. There is already a large field of oncolytics in veterinary science, but it's mainly palliative, and such

PROFILE
Biohacker **Andrew Hessel** founded the Pink Army Cooperative, an open-source drug company. He is also a distinguished researcher in the Bio/Nano/Programmable Matter group at software firm Autodesk, based in San Rafael, California

processes have as many side effects in dogs and cats as in humans because vets are really just repurposing human therapies. If we can prove the technology in the animal model, it will provide the foundation for the third step – starting work with humans.

What about regulatory hurdles for personalised cancer treatments with no clinical trials?
The question I always get is what am I going to do about the US Food and Drug Administration? But when you're working with N-of-1 medicines, regulatory concerns are the last of your worries. Really you make the drug for the individual, so at the end of the day it's the individual who has to choose whether to take it or not. You're always going to be working with someone who has no other pharmaceutical options, and the FDA has allowed such "compassionate use" in similar cases.

How much will your treatments cost?
I want N-of-1 treatments for humans to be free. I never want to sell a drug. I see the business model shifting away from the blockbuster-drug model of the pharma industry – getting the best product for the most people and charging the most for it – to more of a Netflix model, in which you might purchase a subscription for all-that-you-need medicines to manage your cancer. So I see the designs for human cancer treatments, maybe even the designs of other disease treatments, being very nearly free.

How will that be sustainable?
Let's just say this: if the digital pathway is robust, I'm pretty sure I can get the virus-printing costs down to a dollar a dose. The virus itself is designed by algorithms using diagnostic data from the patient. That info is put into a program that will design the cancer-fighting virus, so the cost of design is cheap. Then there's testing, and there is no simpler test than on the patient's own cancer cells in a dish. So that whole process should cost less than $100 end-to-end. If you are on a cancer-subscription model paying $100 a month, I see that as ultimately profitable.

You're clearly not in it for the money...
If I wanted to make money tomorrow, there are other areas of virus engineering that have a much lower bar because they don't deal with human therapeutics. But as the tech platform develops and we start treating animals and doing N-of-1 studies, the mindset will change and then no one will ever again be able to charge a billion dollars to go and make a cancer drug. ∎

Time to enlist life-saving, gutsy allies

A surprising new front is opening up in the war on cancer. We just need to get a few trillion foot soldiers on side, says **Christian Jobin**

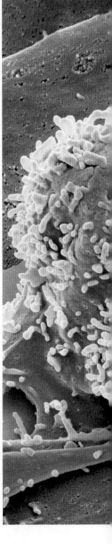

There are subtle links between cancer cells (tinted green) and gut microbes (orange)

THE human body is occupied by trillions of microorganisms, acquired at birth and maintained throughout our lifetime. Though we are mostly oblivious to this microbiome, it forms an intimate and essential part of our being. It is involved in many vital biological processes such as nutrition, the immune system and even mental health. Now evidence is mounting that the microbiome plays a role in cancer too.

In the past five years a comprehensive catalogue of the microorganisms living on and in the different surfaces and cavities of our bodies has been created – a sort of "getting to know your neighbours". This has revealed that the microbiome is a diverse community of more than 1500 species, with the vast majority residing in the intestine. We are just beginning to discover how these microbes influence the development and treatment of cancer.

The first evidence that "friendly" gut bacteria might have a darker side comes from studies in rodents, which developed fewer tumours when their microbiome had been wiped out, indicating the tumour-promoting potential of gut microbes.

In humans, the strongest evidence of the potential role of the microbiome in cancer comes from studies on colorectal cancer (CRC) – the third commonest form of cancer in the US and that country's second leading cause of cancer deaths. Recent research on people with CRC showed that their intestinal microbial communities become unbalanced. For example, compared with healthy people, the stools of people with CRC contain less of the bacterial groups *Lachnospiraceae* and *Roseburia* but an increased abundance of

others such as *Enterococcus* and *Streptococcus*.

Why does it matter which types of microorganisms are present in the gastrointestinal tract? Not only does the microbiome play a key role in our immune system, but it also produces 10 per cent of our energy and ferments dietary carbohydrates into a range of metabolites such as the short-chain fatty acids acetate, propionate and butyrate.

These compounds serve as energy sources and also perform various key immunological and anti-carcinogenic functions in the body. Butyrate, for example, is a major energy source for the cells lining the intestine and also helps counteract inflammation and cancer development in the colon. Consequently, it is likely that an alteration of the microbiome's composition would have repercussions on the health of its host.

How might a "dysbiotic" microbiome play a role in cancer? *Roseburia* microbes, for instance, produce high quantities of butyrate, so fewer of these organisms in the intestines could result in smaller amounts of protective butyrate. Studies in mice showed that low levels of colonic butyrate could foster the development of CRC.

These are interesting findings, but it is not yet known whether a dysbiotic microbiome is a cause of CRC, or arises as a result of it. Nevertheless, these studies suggest a new way of identifying people at risk of developing CRC, through identifying markers of this distinctive microbiota. Potential microbial candidates have already been identified and tested using animal models. For example, samples of strains of *E. coli* and *Fusobacterium*

nucleatum obtained from individuals with CRC were found to promote tumour development when introduced in mice.

It is important to stress that the microbes associated with CRC are not infectious pathogens, but rather indigenous residents of the intestine whose numbers and activities have been altered. This "enemy within" concept contrasts sharply with the infection paradigm, in which infectious microorganisms enter the body and cause harm. The environmental conditions under which our native microorganisms fluctuate in their numbers or change their niche in the body is unclear. But once we find out more about this process,

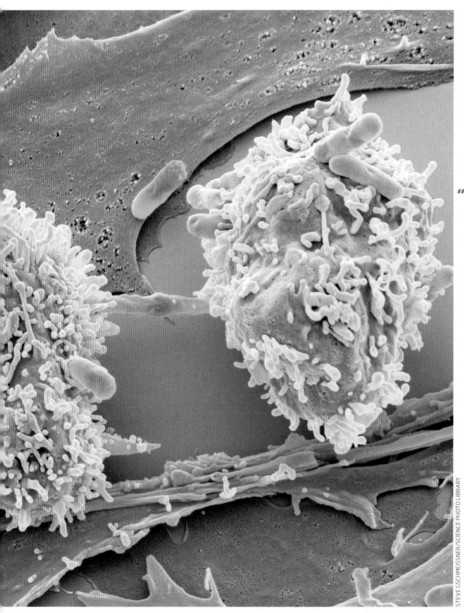

cancer therapy. This field of "bacteriotherapy" is still young, but it might one day be possible to screen individuals at risk of developing CRC for particular biomarkers of a dysbiotic microbiome, and then nudge their unbalanced microbiota back towards a healthier composition. This kind of therapy has been used with great success for recurrent cases of *Clostridium difficile* infection.

What about cancer treatment? Does our microbiome also affect how we react to chemotherapy? Two key studies published

"The interplay of cancer and our microbiome is still a frontier area"

in *Science* in 2013 showed that it does, and highlighted the important role that gut bacteria play in shaping the body's immune response to cancer. One study, by a team of researchers at several laboratories in France, showed that when the intestinal microbiota of mice with cancer were wiped out using antibiotics, this severely compromised the effectiveness of the chemotherapy drug cyclophosphamide. The researchers found that cyclophosphamide causes certain gut microbes to enter the lymph system, where they activate anti-tumour cells. These findings highlight a hitherto unknown risk associated with using antibiotics during chemotherapy treatment.

The other study, led by researchers at the US National Cancer Institute in Maryland, showed that gut bacteria can control the response to cancer therapy by influencing the level of inflammation around the tumour. It found that certain gut microbes enhance the efficacy of anticancer drugs by boosting immune cells' production of a substance called tumour necrosis factor, a messenger molecule which is part of the anticancer immune response.

The interplay of cancer and the microbiome is still a frontier area, but these studies highlight the complex and wide effect of microbes on cancer development and treatment. Once we know more about the microbiome, it may be possible to manipulate it using diet to boost the abundance or activity of microbes with cancer-fighting potential. Alternatively, inhibitors could be designed to target microbial genes implicated in tumour formation, for example to block the enzymes which produce harmful substances such as colibactin.

In the near future I expect that new therapeutic options for cancer will open up, courtesy of our microbiota. ■

this knowledge could be used to manipulate microbial levels, to enhance protective functions and alleviate harmful ones.

How else could gut microbes play a role in cancer? Recent evidence indicates that bacteria may produce noxious agents – gases, toxins, radical oxygen species – that can cause instabilities in the host's genetic material. For instance, the bacterium *E. coli* is found in abundance in the intestinal mucosa of people with CRC, compared with people without CRC. Interestingly, genomic analysis of these CRC-associated *E. coli* revealed the presence of a cluster of genes responsible for producing a substance called colibactin. This natural

product triggers DNA breakage and genomic instability in different cells, including cells lining the intestine. In this case, the activity of the *E. coli* is directly compromising the integrity of the host DNA, which probably contributes to the development of tumours.

Other intestinal bacteria, such as *F. nucleatum*, appear to promote cancer through the action of molecules it produces, which bind to the cells lining the intestine, triggering these cells to proliferate out of control.

All this research is indicating that microbes could not only be used as a predictor of CRC onset, but also be manipulated as part of

STEVE GSCHMEISSNER/SCIENCE PHOTO LIBRARY

Healed in the
womb

Imagine being able to cure disease before it even arises. We already have the technology, discovers **Meera Senthilingam**, if only we dare to use it

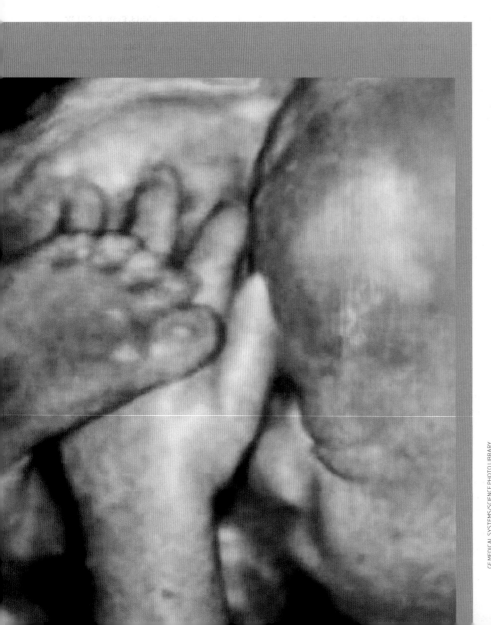

OUR time in the womb is one of the most vulnerable periods of our existence. Pregnant women are warned to steer clear of certain foods and alcohol, and doctors refrain from medical interventions unless absolutely necessary, to avoid the faintest risk of causing birth defects.

Yet it is this very stage that is now being considered for some of the most daring and radical medical procedures yet devised: stem cell and gene therapies. "It's really the ultimate preventative therapy," says Alan Flake, a surgeon at the Children's Hospital of Philadelphia in Pennsylvania. "The idea is to avoid any manifestations of disease."

The idea may sound alarming, but there is a clear rationale behind it. Use these therapies on an adult, and the body part that you are trying to fix is fully formed. Use them before birth, on the other hand, and you may solve the problem before it even arises. "This will set a new paradigm for treatment of many genetic disorders in future," says Flake.

Flake has been performing surgery on unborn babies for nearly 30 years, using techniques refined on pregnant animals to ensure they met the challenges of working on tiny bodies and avoided triggering miscarriage. The first operation on a human fetus took place in 1981 to fix a blocked urethra, the tube that carries urine out of the bladder. Since then the field has grown to encompass many types of surgery, such as correction of spinal cord defects to prevent spina bifida.

While fetal surgery may now be mainstream, performing stem cell therapy or gene therapy in the womb would arguably be an order of magnitude more challenging. Yet these techniques seem to represent the future of medicine, offering the chance to vanquish otherwise incurable illnesses by re-engineering the body at the cellular level. Several groups around the world are currently testing them out on animals in the womb.

Of the two, stem cell therapy has the longer history: we have been carrying it out on adults since the 1950s, in the form of bone marrow transplants. Bone marrow contains stem cells that give rise to all the different blood cells, from those that make up the immune system to the oxygen-carrying red blood cells. Bone marrow transplants are mainly carried out to treat cancers of immune cells, such as leukaemia, or the various genetic disorders of red blood cells that give rise to anaemia.

One of Flake's interests is sickle-cell disease, in which red blood cells are distorted into a sickle shape by a mutation in the gene for haemoglobin. People with the condition are usually treated with blood transfusions and drugs to ease the symptoms, but even so they may well die in their 40s or 50s. Some are offered a bone marrow transplant, although perhaps only 1 in 3 can find a donor who is a good match genetically and whose cells are thus unlikely to be rejected by their body. "The biggest issue with treating disease with stem cells is the immune system," says Flake.

And therein lies the main reason for trying a bone marrow transplant in an unborn baby: its immune system is not fully formed. At around the fourteenth week of pregnancy, the fetus's immune system learns not to attack its own body, by killing off any immune cells that react to the fetus's own tissues. This raises the prospect of introducing donor stem cells during this learning window and so fooling the immune system into accepting those cells. "You can develop a state of complete tolerance to the donor," says Flake. "If it works for sickle cell, then there are at least 30 related genetic disorders that could be treated."

Perfect donor

The perfect donor is the mother. For starters, she shares half her genes with the fetus and so is more likely to be a close match. More importantly, if the donated cells cross the placenta into the mother's bloodstream, they will not trigger a maternal immune response which could harm both mother and baby – as well as kill the donated cells.

As with adult bone marrow transplants, the donor cells can simply be injected into the recipient's bloodstream and will find their way to the fetal bone marrow. The mother's bone marrow cells don't need to replace her child's faulty cells: animal studies suggest that even if only a minority of the offspring's bone marrow cells come from the donor, this would be enough to prevent or at least significantly alleviate sickle-cell anaemia. But the real beauty of the treatment is that even if few donor cells survive, they can be topped up after birth by a further bone marrow transplant from the mother, without risk of rejection. It would be like having an identical twin at the ready as a lifelong donor.

So far prenatal bone marrow transplants have only been tried in a handful of cases involving rare genetic disorders. With one exception, results have generally been poor, although those attempts differed from Flake's current approach in several ways: donor cells did not come from the mother, for instance,

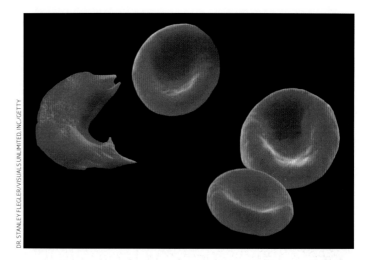
Fetal stem cell therapy could cure sickle-cell disease

DR. STANLEY FLEGLER/VISUALS UNLIMITED, INC./GETTY

or the cells were injected too late in the pregnancy to fool the fetal immune system. "We have spent many years in animal models defining the barriers that caused human attempts to fail," says Flake. He has had promising results in dogs with the canine equivalent of sickle-cell disease. "We've reached a point that encourages me we can do the same thing in humans," he says.

Yet there are still dangers. Any kind of injection into a fetus during the first three months of pregnancy carries a risk of miscarriage of between 1 and 5 per cent. The question is whether the potential benefits outweigh this risk. "This is a lifelong treatment," says Jerry Chan of the KK Women's and Children's Hospital in Singapore who is working on stem cell treatments for thalassaemia – another type of anaemia –

> "Gene therapy has been haunted by the spectre of handing down mutations to future generations"

which he hopes to bring to clinical trials within five years. He is also developing a stem cell therapy for osteogenesis imperfecta, a congenital bone disorder, and have treated two patients with promising results.

Work on gene therapy has likewise been going on for many years. There have been safety concerns, in particular after a US teenager died and other children developed leukaemia, but a couple of adult treatments have reached the clinic: one in China for cancer and one in Europe for a rare metabolic disorder disrupting fat breakdown.

As is the case with adults, gene therapy would only be considered for a fetus if it has a condition that is either fatal or would cause a great deal of suffering. "The diseases most amenable to gene therapy are the ones where there's absolutely no cure or a poor prognosis after birth," says Simon Waddington, who leads the Gene Transfer Technology group at University College London (UCL).

Once again, there are advantages to intervening in the womb, besides the principle that prevention is better than cure. The fetus's small size means that for a given dose of therapeutic DNA, a bigger proportion of its cells will be changed. "There is a clear case for going in early," says Waddington.

There is another benefit: most gene therapies use a viral vector, a virus modified to deliver the therapeutic DNA into cells. Adults sometimes mount an immune response against the virus; babies in the womb do not as they have not yet encountered it.

The team at UCL is focusing its efforts on treating rare genetic disorders of the liver and its metabolism. Symptoms do not appear in the womb, because the mother's liver performs the fetus's metabolic functions. After birth, the baby's own liver fails to kick in.

One such condition, Gaucher disease, is caused by the lack of an enzyme needed to metabolise certain fatty molecules. Its absence leads to the build-up of toxins throughout the body, with one form of the disease damaging nerve cells and causing extensive brain damage. Children with this condition live for only two or three years.

Waddington's colleague Ahad Rahim has used a viral vector to deliver a copy of the missing gene into mice that have the equivalent of Gaucher disease. The therapy ➤

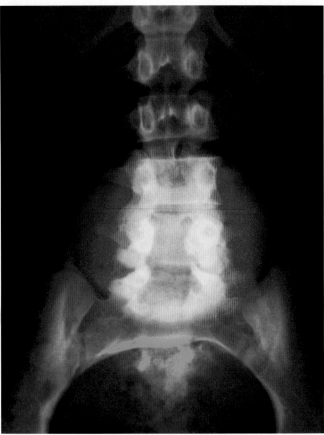

SCIENCE PHOTO LIBRARY

Surgery in the womb
to treat spina bifida is
now routine

is injected into the fetus's bloodstream and can be given later in the pregnancy, so the risk of miscarriage should, in theory, be minimal.

In mice, the viral vector spreads through the brain, nerves and the rest of the body. "We want it to spread," says Rahim. Such broad take-up is helpful as Gaucher disease affects the brain, spleen, muscles and limbs as well as the liver.

But delivery through the bloodstream raises another issue. Since the idea of gene therapy was first mooted, it has been haunted by the spectre of generating harmful mutations that could be handed down to future generations. The central dogma has thus been to avoid tampering with the "germ line", in other words, people's sperm and eggs. "There has always been that concern that you might affect the germ line," says Waddington.

The fetal cells that go on to become sperm and eggs develop in a compartment that is relatively impermeable to the bloodstream. Their isolation takes place around the seventh week of pregnancy. In theory, gene therapies given after this stage should not reach them. "The risk is pretty low," says Waddington.

Choosing the appropriate viral vector also reduces the risk. Some types of gene therapy use a virus that inserts itself into the patient's DNA, so when cells divide the new gene is passed on to daughter cells indefinitely. The

UCL team use a virus called AAV, which sits next to the DNA without integrating into it.

That means that even if the virus reaches the sperm and egg precursor cells, it should not be copied when they divide. "There is more concern over germ line transmission with integrating vectors," says Waddington.

The germ line question should be resolved in the next few years, as various trials using AAV are carried out in macaques, an animal model that should more closely resemble what would happen in humans. Previous trials using integrating viruses have shown little germ line transmission, and use of AAV should cause even less.

Germ line target?

Whatever the results, however, interfering with the germ line may no longer be the no-no it once was, according to Julian Savulescu, a bioethicist at the University of Oxford and editor of the *Journal of Medical Ethics*. "If the intervention were safe and [led to a cure], it would be highly desirable if this were passed on to the next generation," he says.

As Waddington points out, if his approach saves a child's life without correcting their sperm or eggs, "we're making people viable that otherwise wouldn't be viable". Looked at that way, if the goal is to avoid handing down

mutations to future generations, then targeting the germ line is positively desirable.

However, most see germ line transmission as something to avoid. "As soon as you start getting into germ line transmission you are entering new ethical territory that at the moment you're not allowed to enter, and for good reason," says Andrew George, who heads the UK's Gene Therapy Advisory Committee. "You are talking about passing on something that is going to have a life beyond the individual you're treating."

It is hard to predict when these kinds of techniques could move from animals into people. Chan reckons that babies in the womb could be receiving his stem cell treatment by 2018. Others, like Flake, prefer not to be drawn on timescales.

The idea of prenatal therapy has been given new impetus by recent advances in genetic sequencing techniques; it is now possible to sequence a fetus's genes without risk of miscarriage, simply using fetal cells that reach the mother's blood. "It is very possible that whole-genome sequencing will become standard procedure for prenatal care," says Chiara Bacchelli of the UCL Institute of Child Health. At the moment these sorts of rare genetic disorders may be discovered only when a family's first child gets ill.

The field has also been buoyed by the go-ahead for a large project aimed at developing gene therapy for pregnant women rather than the fetus. The aim is to treat fetal growth restriction, a condition caused by lack of blood flow to the placenta on the mother's side. In extreme cases, this can cause fetal death or brain damage, and it is responsible for most stillbirths seen today.

Signs are usually picked up at the 24-week scan during pregnancy, but as yet nothing can be done. "This condition is currently untreatable," says Anna David, an obstetrician at UCL who is running the trial.

The treatment is to deliver a gene coding for a chemical signal called vascular endothelial growth factor to blood vessels on the maternal side of the placenta, which should boost their growth. "Success would show it is possible to do these very difficult gene therapy trials in pregnant women," says David. If so, that might ease the way for fetal trials.

It's a big if. But it raises the prospect of a world without such debilitating illnesses as sickle-cell anaemia and Gaucher disease. "Why not predict things happening before birth and stop any damage occurring?" asks Waddington. "If you can stop this before it happens, isn't that the perfect situation?" ∎

Miracle cells

Stem cells could repair almost any injury and treat any disease, and we are on the brink of harnessing them.
Helen Thomson is your guide

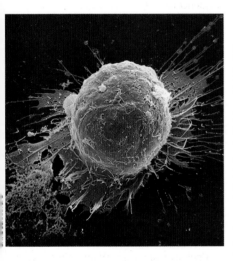

A BLIND woman receives the gift of sight. A paralysed man walks again. A woman finds her voice after years of silence. These may sound like biblical miracles, but all happened for real in the past few years. The modern-day saviour? Stem cells.

These phenomenal yet controversial cells hold incredible promise in medicine. As well as repairing eyes, spinal cords and larynxes, their miraculous healing power is being extended to conditions as diverse as Parkinson's disease, diabetes, rheumatoid arthritis, cancer, Alzheimer's disease and even baldness.

That's because stem cells are the blank slate that every kind of tissue in our bodies started out as. Learning to control them would give us the power to manufacture any cell we want.

In nature there are three different kinds of stem cell. The most powerful are totipotent cells, which form right after an egg is fertilised and can become any type of cell in the body or placenta. Then there are pluripotent cells, more commonly referred to as embryonic stem cells (ESCs). These appear around four days after an egg is fertilised and can form any cell except for those that make up the placenta. ESCs currently have the best prospects as medical treatments but their use is highly contentious, since harvesting them means destroying an embryo.

Finally there are adult stem cells. They occur naturally in the body in places like bone marrow, blood, the gut and liver, where their job is to produce replacements as cells wear out. They are less controversial but also less potent, capable of forming only a narrow range of cell types. These cells have long been indirectly used in medicine, in therapies such as bone marrow transplants to treat blood cancers.

The term "stem cell" was coined by Russian histologist Alexander Maksimov in 1908, when he showed that all blood cells come from a common precursor. The first bone marrow transplant was performed in 1956, but it was not until 1981 that the possibility of using stem cells directly started to look like a possibility. That year saw the first embryonic stem cells extracted from a mouse. The next big milestone came in 1998, when James Thomson at the University of Wisconsin-Madison and colleagues found a way to grow ESCs in culture. Then, in 2006, researchers in Japan worked out how to reprogram ordinary cells – skin cells, for example – by adding four genes to make what are called induced pluripotent stem cells (iPSCs).

Not quite there yet

The creation of iPSCs appeared to be the key that would unlock the full potential of stem cells. It eliminated the ethically troublesome need to destroy embryos and also reduced the risk of immune rejection, since the cells could be derived from the person who needed them.

Unfortunately, they didn't turn out to be the panacea we hoped for. Serious problems soon emerged, involving incomplete reprogramming and a propensity for transplanted iPSCs to form tumours. The viruses used to genetically alter the cells seemed to switch on cancer-causing genes. ❯

"The mix spontaneously forms tiny little livers, just like it does in the womb"

Techniques have improved since then, and in 2014, a 70-year-old woman with macular degeneration – the most common cause of blindness in people over 50 – received the world's first iPSC treatment in the form of a retinal cell graft made out of skin cells from her arm. News of her progress is expected at the end of 2015.

Our enhanced understanding of iPSCs is also making it possible to improve on some of the trials carried out in the past. For example, 20 years ago, scientists tried transplanting tiny amounts of brain tissue from aborted fetuses into the brains of people with Parkinson's. They believed the tissue would grow and replace some of the dopamine-producing neurons ravaged by the disease.

"When it worked, it worked beautifully," says Jeanne Loring, who led the study at the Scripps Institute in La Jolla, California.

However, when it didn't, there were severe consequences. Some of the fetal tissue grew into other types of brain cell, which caused side effects such as a disorder called dyskinesia, in which people lose the ability to control muscle movements. The trial was halted.

Now, Loring's team plans to try again using iPSCs. They have coaxed skin cells to turn into early stage dopamine-producing neurons and are currently gearing up to apply for approval to transplant them into the people who provided the cells.

Embryonic stem cells are also progressing. In 2011, Geron, a biotech giant based in Menlo Park, California, got the green light to perform a small trial in four people with spinal cord injuries. Geron researchers used ESCs to grow early neuroglia cells, which support and insulate nerves, and these were injected where the injury had occurred. However, we don't yet know how the participants fared, since the company shut down the trial soon after they were treated, citing financial difficulties.

The first real success was in 2012, when two people with degenerative eye diseases were given implants of retinal cells made from ESCs. Four months later, there were no negative side effects and, better still, both had improved vision. More people were given the treatment and so far it seems to be working well. "One of the patients can now use a computer and read her watch; another can see well enough to ride a horse," says Robert Lanza at Advanced Cell Technology in Marlborough, Massachusetts, the company that performed the treatment.

Electrically duped

There is also life in an older technique called somatic cell nuclear transfer (SCNT), which was famously used to clone Dolly the sheep in 1996. This involves taking the nucleus from a fetal or infant cell and placing it into an empty egg. Applying a few chemicals and a jolt of electricity fools the egg into thinking it is fertilised, at which point it starts to form an embryo. You can then

Adult stem cells	Embryonic stem cells	Somatic cell nuclear transfer	Induced pluripotent stem cells
Extracted directly from body	Extracted from blastocyst	Cloned embryo created by inserting cell nucleus into egg	Genes used to reprogram adult cell

Attributes			
Proven success	Pluripotent – can form nearly all types of cell Plentiful	Pluripotent	Pluripotent Plentiful Can be made from person's own cells so no immune concerns
Limitations			
Limited in number Can only form some types of cell	Risk of adverse immune response Involves destruction of embryo	Relies on donated egg Involves creation and destruction of embryo	Technology relatively new Cancer risk? Incomplete programming?
Uses so far			
• Multiple uses, eg bone marrow transplant for leukaemia, multiple sclerosis • 2008 New windpipe	• 2012 trial – retinal cells made from ESCs implanted in people with degenerative eye disease	• 1996 Dolly the sheep • Therapeutic cloning • 2014 Insulin-producing cells	• 2014 Six people with degenerative eye disease given retinal cells made of iPSCs • 2013 New liver, implanted in mice

MATT DUNHAM/AP/PRESS ASSOCIATION IMAGES

Stem cells have already
been used to build new
body parts

harvest embryonic stem cells from your newly
formed therapeutic clone.

In 2014, researchers proved it was possible
to perform the technique using an adult
human cell. The team took skin cells from
a woman with diabetes and used SCNT to
transform them into insulin-producing beta
cells. These could theoretically be used to
replace the ones destroyed by her disease –
though SCNT remains ethically challenging
because it involves creating a human embryo.

That is one major reason why researchers
continue to explore new avenues for making
stem cells. In the early part of 2014 came the
tantalising possibility of a remarkably simple
technique that would eliminate the ethical
issues altogether.

The technique, announced in two *Nature*
papers, purported to be able to make
pluripotent stem cells simply by giving adult
cells a 30-minute bath in acid: no viruses, no
genes, no discarded embryos. "I don't think for
one moment people thought this might be
possible in humans," said Chris Mason,
professor of regenerative medicine at
University College London, at the time.

It turned out Mason's instincts were right.
Over the next few months the work was slowly
torn apart by researchers around the world.

SUTTON HIBBERT/REX

An early stem cell success:
Dolly the sheep was born
in 1996

"I can't find the words to apologise," lead
author Haruko Obokata of the Riken Institute
in Kobe, Japan, eventually said, after failing to
repeat her experiments under supervision.
She was found guilty of scientific misconduct
and *Nature* retracted both papers.

The saga also claimed another victim.
Yoshiki Sasai, a member of Obokata's team
who was cleared of direct misconduct but had
faced criticism for his oversight, was found
dead in his lab in an apparent suicide. His
death was called "a true tragedy for science" by
Nature's editor-in-chief, Phil Campbell – and it
illustrates the pressure of expectation and
hope under which stem cell scientists are
working.

Despite this setback, progress has continued
apace. For example, why stop at replacing bits
of tissue, when you can grow whole organs?
In 2008, the first transplant of a full human
organ grown from stem cells gave a Colombian
woman a new trachea.

Her windpipe had been destroyed by
tuberculosis, so researchers harvested a
section of donated trachea and stripped away
its cells to leave a scaffold. This framework was
seeded with stem cells from the woman's bone
marrow, then grown in a lab before being
implanted in her throat.

Meanwhile, researchers at Yokohama City
University in Japan have been using stem cells
to grow organs from scratch. Takanori Takebe
and his colleagues converted human skin
cells into iPSCs, and then enticed them into
becoming liver cells. Mix into the recipe some
mesenchymal stem cells – which produce fat,
bone and cartilage – and some blood vessel
cells, and the concoction spontaneously forms
tiny little livers, just as happens in the womb.
When these livers were placed in mice, they
linked up with blood vessels, grew and
performed a whole range of healthy liver
functions.

Although there have been trials,
tribulations and techniques that were
too good to be true, it's clear that the
possibilities for stem cells are enormous.
But it is still early days. "We have to stop
ourselves because we keep coming up with
things you can do with stem cells to help in
virtually any disease, and you can't stretch
yourself too thin," says Loring. "But it's so
difficult to hold back, because their potential
is amazing. Just endless." ∎

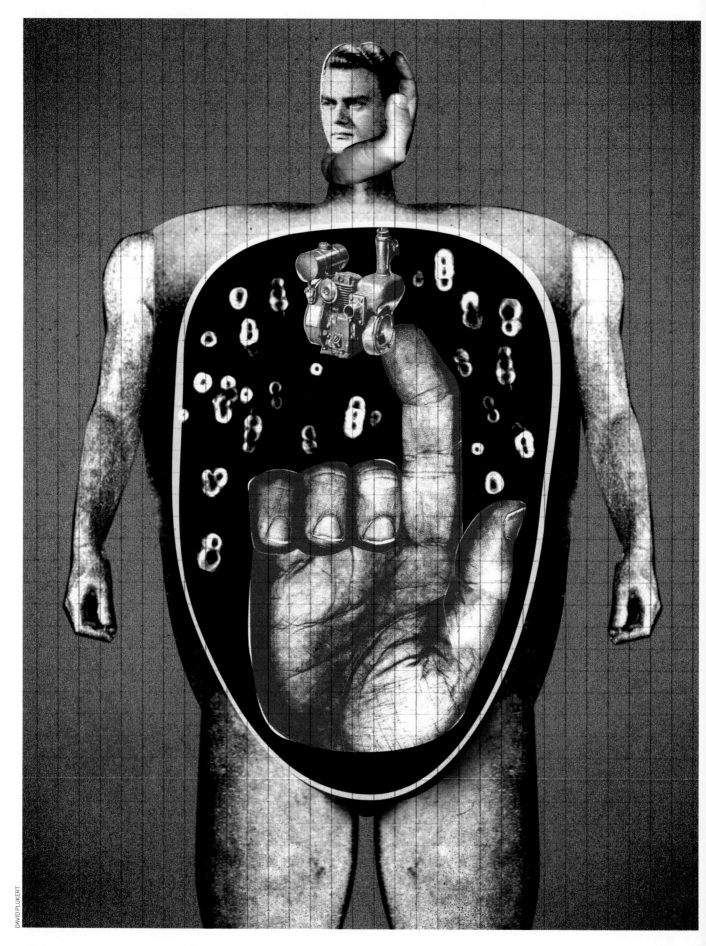

DAVID PLUKERT

The secret to repairing our bodies and growing new organs is getting all touchy-feely, says Bob Holmes

Let's get physical

YOU started life as a single cell. Now you are made of many trillions. There are more cells in your body than there are stars in the galaxy. Every day billions of these cells are replaced. And if you hurt yourself, billions more cells spring up to repair broken blood vessels and make new skin, muscle or even bone.

Even more amazing than the staggering number of cells, though, is the fact that, by and large, they all know what to do – whether to become skin or bone and so on. The question is, how?

"Cells don't have eyes or ears," says Dennis Discher, a biophysical engineer at the University of Pennsylvania in Philadelphia.

'Simply expose stem cells to flowing fluid and they turn into blood vessels"

"If you were blind and deaf, you'd get around by touch and smell. You'd feel a soft chair to sit on, a hard wall to avoid, or whether you're walking on carpet or concrete."

Not long ago, the focus was all on "smell": that is, on how cells respond to chemical signals such as growth factors. Biologists thought of cells as automatons that blindly followed the orders they were given. In recent years, however, it has started to become clear that the sense of touch is vital as well, allowing cells to work out for themselves where they are and what they should be doing. Expose stem cells to flowing fluid, for instance, and they turn into blood vessels.

What is emerging is a far more dynamic picture of growth and development, with a great deal of interplay between cells, genes and our body's internal environment. This may explain why exercise and physical therapy are so important to health and healing – if cells don't get the right physical cues when you are recovering from an injury, for instance, they won't know what to do. It also helps explain how organisms evolve new shapes – the better cells become at sensing what they should do, the fewer genetic instructions they need to be given.

The findings are also good news for people who need replacement tissues and organs. If tissue engineers can just provide the right physical environment, it should make it easier to transform stem cells into specific tissues and create complex, three-dimensional organs that are as good as the real thing. And researchers are now experimenting with ways

of using tactile cues to improve wound healing and regeneration.

Biologists have long suspected that mechanical forces may help shape development. "A hundred years ago, people looked at embryos and saw that it was an incredibly physical process," says Donald Ingber, head of Harvard University's Wyss Institute for Biologically Inspired Engineering. "Then when biochemistry and molecular biology came in, the baby was thrown out with the bathwater and everybody just focused on chemicals and genes."

Although it was clear that physical forces play a role – for example, astronauts living in zero gravity suffer bone loss – until recently there was no way to measure and experiment with the tiny forces experienced by individual cells. Only in the past few years, as equipment like atomic force microscopes has become more common, have biologists, physicists and tissue engineers begun to get to grips with how forces shape cells' behaviour.

One of the clearest examples comes from Discher and his colleagues, who used atomic force microscopy to measure the stiffness of a variety of tissues and gel pads. Then they grew human mesenchymal stem cells – the precursors of bone, muscle and many other tissue types – on the gels. In each case, the cells turned into the tissue that most closely matched the stiffness of the gel.

The softest gels, which were as flabby as brain tissue, gave rise to nerve cells. In contrast, gels that were 10 times stiffer – like muscle tissue – generated muscle cells, and ❯

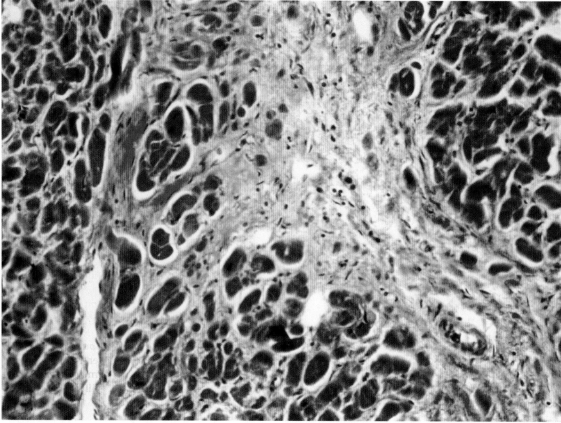

ASTRID & HANNS-FRIEDER MICHLER / SCIENCE PHOTO LIBRARY

Softening scar
tissue could be the
key to regenerating
damaged hearts

yet stiffer gels gave rise to bone. "What's surprising is not that there are tactile differences between one tissue and another," says Discher. After all, doctors rely on such differences every time they palpate your abdomen. "What's surprising is that cells feel that difference."

The details of how they do this are now emerging. Most cells other than blood cells live within a fibrous extracellular matrix. Each cell is linked to this matrix by proteins in its membrane called integrins, and the cell's internal protein skeleton is constantly tugging on these integrins to create a taut, tuned whole. "There's isometric tension that you don't see," says Ingber.

In practice, this means changes in external tension – such as differences in the stiffness of the matrix, or the everyday stresses and strains of normal muscle movement – can be transmitted into the cell and ultimately to the nucleus, where they can direct the cell's eventual fate.

Since stem cells have yet to turn into specific cell types, biologists expected them to be extra sensitive to the environment, and this does indeed seem to be the case. Ning Wang, a bioengineer at the University of Illinois at Urbana-Champaign, found that the embryonic stem cells of mice are much softer than other, more specialised cells. This softness means that tiny external forces can deform the

cells and influence their development.

That's why, when stem cells are exposed to flowing fluid, they turn into the endothelial cells that line the inner surface of blood vessels. In fact, fluid flow – particularly pulses that mimic the effect of a beating heart – is proving crucial for growing replacement arteries in the laboratory. The rhythmic stress helps align the fibres of the developing artery, making them twice as strong, says Laura

"The secret of growing cartilage that is as strong as the real thing is to mimic the effects of walking"

Niklason, a tissue engineer at Yale University. A biotech company Niklason founded, called Humacyte, has begun human trials on arteries grown this way (see also "Rebuild your body", page 82).

Surprisingly, pulsatile motion can help heal injuries in situ too. In the early 2000s, Ingber and his colleague Dennis Orgill began treating patients with difficult-to-heal wounds by implanting a small sponge in the wound and connecting this to a pump. The pump sucks the cells surrounding the wound in and out of the sponge's pores, distorting them by about 15 to 20 per cent. This turned out to be an

almost ideal stimulus for inducing the cells to grow and form blood vessels and thus boost the healing process, says Ingber.

Meanwhile, tissue engineers are finding that they can grow far better bone and cartilage by mimicking the stresses that the tissues normally experience in the body. For instance, human cartilage grown in the lab is usually nowhere near as strong as the real thing. However, Clark Hung, a biomedical engineer at Columbia University in New York City, found a way to grow cartilage that matches its natural counterpart strength for strength. The secret, he found, is rhythmically squeezing the cartilage as it grows to mimic the stress of walking.

Hung says this is partly because the pressure helps to pump nutrients into cartilage, which has no blood vessels. But his experiments suggest that the loading alone also plays an important role. His team hopes the engineered cartilage will eventually be used to resurface arthritic human joints.

Even relatively mild stresses make a big difference. Attempts to grow replacement bone by placing stem cells in a culture chamber of the desired shape have not been very successful, with the cells often dying or producing only weak bone. But Gordana Vunjak-Novakovic, a biomedical engineer also at Columbia, has found that mimicking the internal flow of fluid that growing bones normally experience helps maximise strength. Her team has used this approach to successfully grow a replica of part of the temporomandibular joint in the jaw from human stem cells, producing a naturally shaped, fully viable bone after just five weeks.

"If you don't stimulate bone cells, they don't do much," says Vunjak-Novakovic. "But if you do, they wake up and start making bone at a higher rate."

There is still a long way to go. The replica bone lacks the thin layer of cartilage that lines the real bone, and it also lacks a blood supply, so it begins to starve as soon as it is removed from the culture chamber.

Again, though, the answer could be to provide the cells with the right physical cues. For example, Vunjak-Novakovic has used lasers to drill channels in the scaffolds for growing heart muscle in the lab. When fluid begins flowing through these channels, endothelial cells move in to line them while muscle cells move away. "Each of the cells will find its own niche," she says.

Even small differences in forces can influence development. In 2008, Christopher Chen, now at Boston University, grew flat sheets of mesenchymal stem cells and exposed them to a mixture of growth factors for bone and marrow development. The cells on the edges of the sheets, which were exposed to the greatest stresses, turned into bone cells, while those in the middle turned

"If tissue engineers provide the right physical cues when growing organs, cells will do the rest"

into the fat cells found in marrow, as happens in real bone.

If this kind of sorting out according to physical forces is widespread in development, it could be very good news for tissue engineers. Instead of having to micromanage the process of producing a replacement organ, they need only provide the right cues and let the cells do the rest.

Indeed, it makes a lot of sense for some developmental decisions to be "devolved" to cells. The growth of tissues like muscles, bone, skin and blood vessels has to be coordinated as our bodies develop and adapt to different activities and injuries. A rigid genetic programme could easily be derailed, whereas using tactile cues as guides allows tissues to adapt quickly as conditions change – for instance, carrying heavy loads will make our bones grow stronger.

This kind of plasticity may play a vital role in evolution as well as during the lifetime of individuals. When the ancestors of giraffes acquired mutations that made their necks longer, for instance, they did not have to evolve a whole new blueprint for making necks. Instead, the nerves, muscles and skin

would have grown proportionately without needing further changes in instructions. The result of this plasticity is a developmental programme that is better able to cope with evolutionary changes, says Ingber.

There is, however, a drawback. When disease or injury changes the stiffness of a tissue, things can go awry. Some researchers have suggested that tissue stiffening plays a role in multiple sclerosis, in which nerves lose their protective myelin sheath. It may also play a role in some cancers (see "Lumps and bumps", below).

It could also explain why many tissues fail to heal perfectly after an injury. To prevent infection, the body needs to patch up wounds as quickly as possible. So it uses a form of collagen that is easier to assemble than the normal one. "It's a quick patch, things are sealed off and you go on – but it's not perfect regeneration," says Discher. The quick-fix collagen is stiffer than normal tissue, as anyone with a large scar will tell you.

After a heart attack, for example, the dead portion of the heart muscle scars over. Why, Discher wondered, don't heart muscle cells then replace the scar tissue? To find out, he and his colleagues grew embryonic heart cells on matrixes of differing stiffness. When the matrix was the same stiffness as healthy heart muscle, the cells grew normally and beat happily. But if the matrix was as stiff as scar tissue, the cells gradually stopped beating.

The constant work of trying to flex the stiffer matrix wears the cells out, Discher thinks. "It's like pushing on a brick wall. Finally, they give up."

Discher believes the solution may lie in finding a way to soften the scar tissue so that heart cells can repopulate it (see also "Heart, heal thyself", page 78). Several enzymes, such as matrix metalloproteinases and collagenases, might do the job, but overdoing it could be risky. "If you degrade the matrix too much, you lose the patch," he warns.

The stiffness of scar tissue may also prevent regeneration in nerve injury, because nerve cells prefer the softest of surroundings. "It might just be that the growing tip of the axon senses that there's a stiff wall ahead of it and doesn't grow through because of that," speculates Jochen Guck, a biophysicist at the University of Cambridge who studies nerve growth after injury.

There is still a long way to go before we fully understand how cells sense and respond to the forces on them. But it is becoming clear that the touchy-feely approach could be the key to regenerating the body. ∎

LUMPS AND BUMPS

Many tumours are stiffer than the tissues in which they form – after all, doctors often first detect many cancers of organs such as the breast and prostate by feeling a hard lump. Some researchers now suspect that this stiffness is not always just a consequence of the cancer. It may be a cause as well.

A team led by Paul Janmey, a biophysicist at the University of Pennsylvania in Philadelphia, has found that the cycle of cell division in breast cells stops when they are grown on a soft gel, keeping them in a quiescent state. Anything that signals stiffness – even just touching a cell with a rigid probe – can be enough to start division again.

Similarly, when Valerie Weaver, a cancer biologist at the University of California at San Francisco, and her team used chemicals to soften the extracellular matrix in which breast cells were growing in the lab, they found the cells were less likely to become malignant. This might help explain why women with denser breast tissue are more likely to develop breast cancer.

Some researchers, too, have reported seeing tumours form around the scars from breast-implant surgery. "This needs to be looked at again," says Weaver. If the link exists, it might be possible to block tumour growth by interfering with the way cells detect stiffness.

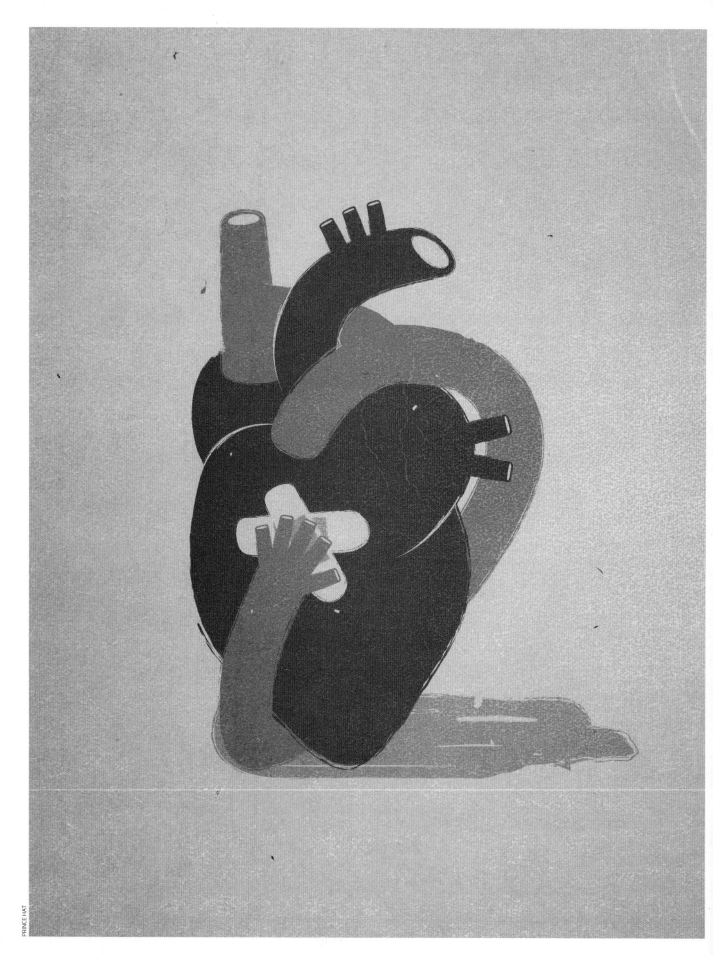

HEART, HEAL THYSELF

If we can't fix hearts with stem cells there might be an even better way, discovers Linda Geddes

IT STARTS slowly, with a faint discomfort that grows until it feels like a vice is tightening around your chest. The pain radiates to your left arm and shoulder, and to the back of your neck. You feel sick, dizzy and short of breath. When the pain passes, you wonder what on earth just happened. In one way you can consider yourself lucky: you have just survived a heart attack.

But your troubles are far from over. When the blood supply to part of your heart was blocked, the muscle cells there died. As the dead cells are replaced by scar tissue, more and more strain will be put on the rest of the heart, causing it to enlarge and slowly fail.

This is the fate of millions of people around the world. Yet if the dead area of their hearts could be replaced with new muscle tissue, their lives would be transformed. A few years ago, doctors thought they might have the answer. They hoped that damaged hearts could be fixed by extracting stem cells from people and injecting them into the heart.

The bad news is that this approach seems to do little good. But the work has not been in vain. It has led to a series of discoveries that promise to provide better ways of regenerating the heart.

Not so long ago, few researchers entertained any hopes of heart regeneration. Although some fish and amphibians can grow new muscle if their hearts are damaged, mammals cannot. Break a human heart, and its cells will stubbornly refuse to grow back again.

But what if you could grow new cells outside the body and get them to turn into new heart muscle? This idea really took off around 2000, when it was shown that stem cells in our bone marrow have the potential to turn into heart muscle cells. If you extracted these stem cells and injected them into the heart, the thinking went, they would turn into muscle and replace any damaged tissue. "The field went through a phase of 'have cells, will inject'," says Rahul Aras, head of Juventas Therapeutics in Cleveland, Ohio.

While some early animal trials produced dramatic results, the results of human trials so far have been disappointing. Any improvements in heart function are usually slight, and some people developed an irregular heartbeat after certain types of cells were injected. Biologists certainly haven't given up on the idea of repairing the heart with stem cells, though. Some are experimenting with different kinds, such as embryonic stem cells, for example. Others think it might not be necessary to inject any cells at all. Instead, they argue, if only we can discover the right signals, we could persuade the existing stem cells in our bodies to multiply, travel to the heart and repair it.

The hope is that the cells will work their way into the heart over days or weeks, which might be better than a massive one-off dose of stem cells. If it works, "in situ stem cell therapy" would have numerous other advantages over injecting cells. For starters, there would be no need to extract people's bone marrow, which is a painful procedure, and no risk of the stem cells becoming infected or acquiring dangerous mutations when outside the body. It would also be much easier to scale up this approach to treat large numbers of people.

Doctors have long used drugs that stimulate the bone marrow to produce more blood stem cells. Building on this work, in 2009 Sara Rankin of Imperial College London and her colleagues showed that certain combinations of chemical factors make the bone marrow of mice release the kind of marrow stem cells that are capable of turning into muscle. The same chemical cocktail also releases endothelial progenitor cells, which help ❯

form new blood vessels and so might restore blood supply to the heart. "We think these cells are mobilised in the context of normal injury, but we want to enhance that effect," says Rankin.

The procedure releases a flood of stem cells into the blood within hours. It remains to be seen, however, whether this will significantly boost healing in people. Some reckon that what really matters is getting stem cells to go where they are needed.

Marrow stem cells are known to bind to a protein called SDF-1, found on the surface of some other cells. So several companies, including Juventas Therapeutics, hope that getting cells in areas of tissue damage to produce SDF-1 will make stem cells remain in the area and repair the damage. "Mobilised stem cells don't know where to go," says Aras. "We're creating a beacon or a signal as to where the damage has occurred, so those circulating cells move to that target."

In a phase 1 trial, pieces of DNA containing the gene for the SDF-1 were injected into the hearts of 17 people with heart failure, resulting in the temporary production of SDF-1 in some heart cells. After several small trials, 1, in which the treatment appears safe and the results seem promising, the company is moving on to larger studies.

In theory, the best results would come from combining these two approaches: getting the bone marrow to release more stem cells and getting more to stay in the heart where they are needed. But there is a twist in this tale. The whole idea behind this approach – that marrow-derived stem cells will form new heart muscle – now appears mistaken. "The heart is a complex and highly organised

"The mental block we had that the mammalian heart doesn't regenerate is gone"

tissue," says Brock Reeve of the Harvard Stem Cell Institute (and brother of actor Christopher Reeve). "Even though people could create heart muscle cells in vitro, [stem cells] don't organise into heart tissue that can beat at a certain rate when injected into the body."

Nevertheless, they do often seem to help. "A lot of work has now shown that these stem cells can promote the repair of heart tissue following heart attack, but without becoming part of that tissue," says Rankin.

It is now thought that marrow-derived stem cells help by releasing signalling factors that in turn rally local cells to initiate repair, for instance by growing new blood vessels. Juventas Therapeutics says animal studies show that its treatment promotes the growth of blood vessels. While the beneficial effects of marrow cells are not enough to compensate for the billion or so muscle cells lost after a serious heart attack, it's a start.

In particular, bone-marrow-derived stem cells may stimulate division of stem-cell-like cells already living in the heart. Until recently, such resident cells were thought to be rare, if they existed at all. Now it is clear that rather than being born with all the heart cells we will ever have, there is an ongoing slow replacement of heart cells throughout life. The current estimate is that 1 per cent of heart cells

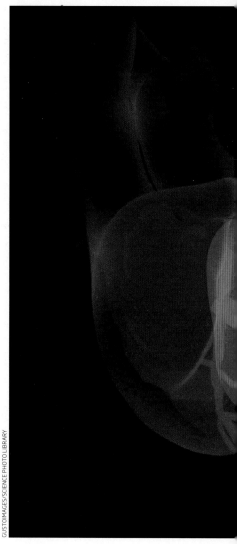
GUSTOIMAGES/SCIENCE PHOTO LIBRARY

are replaced each year in a 25-year-old, but this percentage falls as we age. "The human heart isn't as static as we thought it was," says Paul Riley of the Oxford Stem Cell Institute in the UK. Over the past decade, researchers have begun to identify the heart stem cells responsible for this renewal. Some groups now hope to treat patients by extracting heart stem cells, growing large numbers in the lab and injecting them back into individuals' hearts. The first small human trials produced encouraging results.

Although heart stem cells may prove more effective than bone marrow cells, getting hold of them is riskier. One trial used stem cells extracted from a small piece of heart tissue taken during bypass surgery. If we could identify the correct chemical cues, though, it might not be necessary to extract heart stem cells. "We just need to tap into the mechanisms by which these cells are turned over – and drive it forward," says Riley.

He and his colleagues have identified a population of stem cells in the epicardium, the outermost layer of the tissue that

GROW YOUR OWN

Sometimes a heart is so badly damaged that replacement is the only option. Instead of having to wait for scarce transplants, one day it may be possible to grow new hearts from scratch.

We have already grown relatively simple body parts. People have been implanted with bladders, larynxes and tracheae made by seeding a scaffold with their own cells (see "Miracle cells", page 71). But these are thin-walled structures; the heart is a much greater challenge.

One approach to recreating its 3D structure is to grow sheets of beating heart cells in a dish, and stack them on top of one another to form thick "patches". The sheets synchronise contractions, and when these patches are implanted into injured rat hearts, they even couple with the existing heart cells.

Another approach is to take hearts from people who have died, or animals such as pigs, remove all the cells to leave just a framework made of collagen

and then seed this scaffold with the cells of the individual who needs a new heart. Doris Taylor of the Texas Heart Institute has seeded rat heart scaffolds with stem cells from newborn rats. When hooked up to a blood supply, these hearts beat just as if they were inside a live animal. Researchers are now working on doing the same with pig hearts, though there is a long way to go before such hearts could be used as replacements (see also "Let's get physical", page 74).

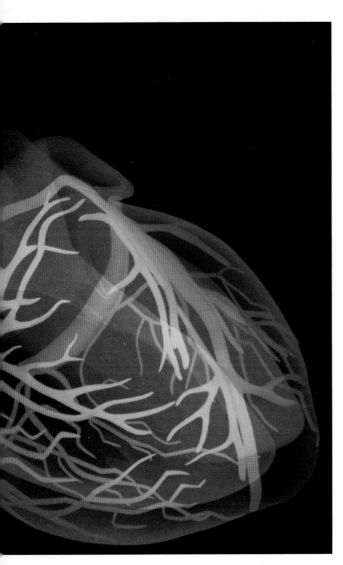

With a little persuasion, hearts may be able to repair themselves

surrounds the heart muscle. These cells can turn into new heart muscle cells following a heart attack.

Even better, Riley discovered a way of activating these cells directly. He found that a chemical called thymosin beta 4, which was already known to promote the development of blood vessels in an embryo's heart, could also trigger the growth of new blood vessels and heart muscle in adult mice. "That's critical, because for the repair of damage following a heart attack you need to replace both the blood vessels and also the muscle that's lost," says Riley.

Unfortunately, the effect of thymosin beta 4 is relatively weak in adults, so it is no miracle cure. Nonetheless, Riley's work is an important

"The work proves chemical factors can boost the healing power of the heart"

proof of principle. It shows that it is indeed possible to use chemical factors to boost the healing power of the heart. His team is now investigating the potential of epicardial stem cells and searching for molecules with a stronger effect.

Even more striking evidence comes from Hesham Sadek of Southwestern University in Dallas, Texas. Last year, he did a rather gruesome experiment. He anaesthetised a baby mouse a day after its birth, and placed it on ice until it stopped breathing and its heart stopped beating.

Then he chopped off the bottom 15 per cent of its heart, exposing the chambers inside. Within minutes, a scab formed over the wound, sealing the chambers from the outside. As the animal was slowly warmed, it began to return to life.

What happened next astounded biologists. Over the coming weeks the scab began to disappear and in its place grew new heart muscle. Just three weeks after its tip was amputated, the mouse's heart had entirely regenerated itself. "It looked completely

normal – indistinguishable from a normal heart," says Sadek.

This was not the only surprise. The missing heart muscle was replaced not by stem cells, but by existing beating heart cells that were somehow being triggered to divide. "We found that they divide very avidly in the newborn heart, but then something happens and this ability to divide is shut off, so in the adult heart that slow turnover of cells is carried out by a stem cell population," says Sadek. "The million-dollar question is what prompted these cells to start dividing?"

Regenerative powers

Already they have some clues. Tiny pieces of RNA called microRNAs play a big role in controlling the activity of cells, and by looking at what happens in the heart during the early days of a mouse's life, Sadek and his collaborators identified a group of microRNAs that regulate the division of heart muscle cells. Blocking these molecules in newborn mice boosted heart muscle cell division. Several research teams are now exploring the role of microRNAs and other molecules in adult heart cells, and a handful so far look promising.

Even if the hearts of mice can be made to regenerate, there is no guarantee that the same is true of humans. However, Sadek says that he was contacted by several heart surgeons in the wake of his paper, who told him that infants bounce back from major heart surgery if it is done within three months of their birth, but do not do nearly so well if operated on later. This suggests the human heart also possesses similar regenerative powers early in life.

"The fact that this happens indicates that maybe we can push this further," says Sadek, who hopes to track the fate of cells in babies undergoing heart surgery in the near future. "The mental block we had that the mammalian heart doesn't regenerate is gone."

All these discoveries are leading to a major shift in thinking. There is still a long way to go before this approach starts helping people with heart disease, but in theory at least, treatments based on stimulating the heart to repair itself should be safer and cheaper than injecting stem cells. In the long run, they have the potential to help far more people.

And the heart could be just the start. If it can regenerate itself, why not other organs like the brain? If these studies have shown us anything, it's that the mammalian body has many tricks up its sleeve. We shouldn't underestimate its ability to surprise us. ■

"Some teams have already
used the matrix to build
entire organs from scratch –
it may even repair brains"

Rebuild your body

Once thought to be mere scaffolding, we now know the matrix inside us can enable regeneration on a scale never seen before. **Andy Coghlan** reports

"IT STARTED as a little sore near my knee, probably a mosquito bite," says Elizabeth Loboa. But the antibiotic ointment wasn't working, and within two weeks what was one wound had become three. From the looks of the wound, her doctor suspected the superbug MRSA and prescribed powerful last-line oral antibiotics. It was at that point that the temptation just became too great. "Instead of taking them, I decided to test a treatment I'd been developing – on myself," she says.

Loboa wasn't just any patient. In her lab at North Carolina State University in Raleigh, the materials engineer had been cooking up a special kind of self-destructing super-bandage capable of healing infected wounds quickly, without scarring or standard antibiotics.

At the heart of Loboa's superplaster is a material that degrades until nothing is left but your own, newly regenerated, healthy cells. What's more, the same trick could one day be used to heal everything from shredded muscle and destroyed digestive tissue to shattered bone. Some researchers have already succeeded in using it to build entire organs from scratch, and it may one day play a role in repairing damaged brains. "It's pretty exciting stuff," says Suchitra Sumitran-Holgersson of the University of Gothenburg in Sweden. "We're trying to create a whole new human being."

So what is this superstuff? In the body, it is known as the extracellular matrix – the stuff that remains if you strip away the living cells from, say, a blood vessel, an organ or a bit of skin. This scaffolding gives the various parts of our body their detailed shape and solidity.

And that's all we used to think it did. "Everyone thought the matrix just holds things together," says Stephen Badylak, a regenerative medicine researcher at the University of Pittsburgh in Pennsylvania, who has been one of the early pioneers of matrix-based therapies. Regenerative medicine researchers had long tried to enlist it to regrow organs, believing only that it was a useful scaffold. In animal trials, for example, they would take a kidney and strip it of native cells using a mild detergent. Then they would use the remaining inert chassis as a template on which to deposit the presumed stars of the show: stem cells that recoat the matrix in live flesh.

But a few years ago, it became clear that the matrix does a lot more than it appears. "Now, we recognise its structure is secondary," says Badylak. "It's got loads of functional roles."

For one thing, the matrix is no biologically mute bystander. While it consists mainly of inanimate structural proteins such as collagen and elastin, it also contains proteins that coax the right cells to be in the right place at the right time. For example, hook-like molecules called fibronectins and integrins provide tailored molecular Velcro for specific cells.

Once these have summoned the right cells, the matrix has another trick up its sleeve: it can coax them to turn into bone, muscle or fat cells, according to the tension to which they are subjected once inside the matrix. In your body, this tension is simply a by-product of the everyday stresses of muscle movement. In the lab, it is done by manipulating the stiffness of the matrix. For example, high tension in the matrix's structure will persuade any incoming stem cells to become muscle or bone. Place them into a saggier matrix and they become fat cells (see also "Let's get physical", page 74).

Finally, having convinced them to develop into the right kind of cell, the matrix also has ways of nourishing them so that they continue to mature into larger structures. Its material contains potent growth factors that help blood vessels form, which provide nourishing oxygen for the growing organs.

Exploiting these properties has revolutionised the way we grow organs. In 2013, Harald Ott of Massachusetts General Hospital in Boston built the world's first ❯

TOMOHIRO INABA

functioning artificial kidney, a wildly complex organ that stem cell researchers have always assumed needed to be grown from scratch using numerous different cell types. Ott was astonished to find that although he fed only two types of cells into a decellularised kidney matrix – blood-like stem cells into the blood vessels, and endothelial cells into the labyrinthine plumbing that filters the blood – all the different kinds of cells formed in the sites where they were supposed to. The kidneys worked so well in rats that Ott is now using similar techniques in projects to build hearts and lungs. His is not the only lab pursuing this goal. "We're working on livers,

"The first results were astounding. We've got guys mountain-biking who couldn't stand up before"

hearts, kidneys, oesophaguses, larynxes and small intestines," says Sumitran-Holgersson.

But organs are not the only things we want to regenerate. Badylak immediately realised that the matrix's location cues could help him solve a different problem – growing muscle. Damaged muscle can regrow to some extent, but if a severe injury destroys too much of one specific muscle group, scar tissue prevents it from growing back. The only alternative is transferring muscle from elsewhere in the body, but that doesn't work very well, says Badylak. Such an injury usually means amputation and a prosthesis.

But what if you could use the matrix to attract and grow muscle from a person's own cells? It would not be the first time: decellularised tracheas from cadavers have been successfully used in patients to create new, fully working tracheas (see "Miracle cells", page 71). So Badylak began a trial in which he used matrix taken from pig bladder to regrow big chunks of muscle in six people who had lost more than half of a muscle in road accidents or other trauma. Ron Strang, a 28-year-old US marine whose quadricep muscle had been destroyed by a roadside bomb in Afghanistan, volunteered. "Ron couldn't even get out of a chair without assistance," says Badylak.

After surgically clearing away all residual scar tissue, Badylak simply placed a strip of matrix into the exposed void, taking care to make it taut enough to signal to the body that it should become muscle, not fat.

The first results were astounding. Six months later, the pig matrix had gone, replaced by a completely new, natural matrix from the volunteers' own bodies – with muscle to match.

"I go out hiking," Strang says, "and I'm able to ride a bike." He has also taken up football and basketball. The other volunteers also improved markedly. "We've got guys mountain-biking who couldn't stand up before," says Badylak. His next goal is to restore at least 25 per cent of lost function to 80 further volunteers.

Building muscle is one thing. But what about rebuilding shattered bone? That's what Carmell Therapeutics in Pittsburgh is trying to do, except that the matrix the company is using is made from human blood. "Our material is effectively a highly concentrated blood clot," says Alan West, who runs the company, a spin-off from Carnegie Mellon University. After successful animal studies, he and his team began a trial in human volunteers.

The dough-like substance carries high concentrations of growth factors known to promote bone repair. In the trial, this "bone putty" was applied to the broken shin bones, or tibiae, of 10 volunteers. The team report that not only did healing happen more quickly with bone putty, the fracture sites were less prone to infection. West is hoping to move onto larger trials and work on other bones.

Superbug battle

Still, there are limits to what a natural matrix can do. Loboa, for example, knew that the human extracellular matrix is not naturally antimicrobial. But she really got to thinking about this problem when a friend went into the hospital for an ankle replacement and the wound became infected with MRSA. "They ended up having to amputate the leg below the knee," she says. It was a wake-up call. "We're learning so much about how to regenerate so many different kinds of tissues," she says, "but how do you keep infection out in the age of drug-resistant superbugs?"

So Loboa began to work on a synthetic matrix that could do just that. It would need to turn slowly into the patient's own tissue without ever exposing the flesh beneath to microbes. "The idea is that it's a bandage that never needs to be changed," she says.

Normally, matrix is harvested from human

or pig cadavers. To create her own version, Loboa began with polylactic acid, a biodegradable material often used in medical implants, and fashioned it into fibres designed to mimic the architecture of skin. "The novelty is what we can do with these fibres," she says. "We can make them solid, porous or hollow."

She chose a porous structure, which could be impregnated with a cocktail of anti-inflammatory drugs and Silvadur, a substance containing small amounts of silver ions that are lethal to most drug-resistant bacteria, including MRSA. The material works in two phases: the first release overwhelms all present bugs, and then a second guard leaks out slowly to destroy any interlopers. The structure dictates how fast the silver ions and other drugs are released. Loboa tested the silver-seeping matrix in pigs: even 4-centimetre long wounds injected with MRSA or *E. coli* bacteria remained pristine.

And after seeing it work so many times in her porcine patients, it was this bandage that she applied to her own wound. That's when the true implications hit home. "I put my scaffold on, and the sores were gone in three days," she says. Soon, the scaffold vanished too, leaving at first a dark scar that itself gradually faded. Loboa published her results in 2014, with one omission. "I'm not including my leg data," she said at the time with a smile.

Synthetic matrix can also be used as a template to build body parts far stronger than those nature provides. One group that could benefit enormously would be the millions of people who undergo kidney dialysis every year.

Dialysis is rough on the body: you need to be hooked into machines that cleanse the blood three times a week, with a large arm vein punctured. To do a few days of the kidneys' work in a few hours, blood must be forced through the system at high speed. This heavy use often makes the veins collapse, so doctors have to continually reopen them. If all else fails, it is possible to graft veins from other parts of the body, but during the months it takes for a grafted vein to mature, a plastic catheterised vein must be inserted that often gets infected. "It's harrowing and painful," says Laura Niklason, a tissue engineer at Yale University.

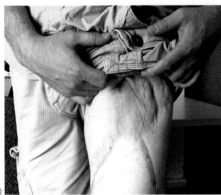

After a bomb ruined Ron Strang's thigh muscles, implanted pig matrix helped regrow them

through the skin or, in the worst cases, into a body cavity. "After 20 years with the disease, about 50 per cent of people will get these," says Eugene Boland, who runs Techshot in Greenville, Indiana, which designs custom medical devices. "And of those, 50 per cent will never heal." The prognosis is grim and untreatable, and includes diapers and constant painkillers.

Working with the University of Louisville in Kentucky, Boland designed a matrix-based plug for the fistula. He used polycaprolactone, a component that, like Loboa's fibres, can be tailored to provide extra niches for cells. He also added fibrinogen, the component of natural matrix that aids wound healing.

Brain rebound

To emplace them into two people with Crohn's, Boland coated the hybrid matrix with surface cells derived from their own fat, and implanted the plugs into fistulas that for years had resisted all treatment. It worked in both cases. "They had closed channels after just two weeks," he says.

The matrix holds a dazzling array of future possibilities. Loboa, for example, is working on a multilayered version that could simultaneously regenerate multiple kinds of tissue damaged in severe accidents. Badylak and others are even beginning to explore its potential for repairing brain damage. Greg Bix of the University of Kentucky in Lexington discovered a key component of the matrix that could promote brain repair all on its own: a signalling molecule released from brain matrix that has been damaged by stroke, called perlecan domain five (DV). It promotes the growth of new blood vessels. When Bix injected DV into mice and rats deliberately given strokes, the results were astounding. "In a fortnight," he says, "you couldn't tell they'd had strokes."

It will be a long time before these treatments become a reality, but Loboa is hopeful that her idea will generate new treatments for skin wounds in the not-too-distant future. And even if major artificial organs are a decade away, as Ott and some of the other researchers assert, matrix can still help heal more commonplace damage to the body, like the muscle, bone and tissue repairs targeted by Badylak and others.

Even simple skin wounds are becoming increasingly dangerous as antibiotic-resistant bacteria thrive in and out of hospitals, and that is where Loboa's change-free bandage could come into its own. "Right now, hospitals are scary places," Loboa says (see "A breath of fresh air", page 30). ■

So Niklason and her colleagues set to work on a making customised natural vein matrix parts that were stronger than the real thing. To do this, they first crafted a fast-decaying biodegradable polymer into a tube exactly the dimensions of a vein, but with a thicker vessel wall. Then they coated this tube with human smooth-muscle cells. Within days, the cells had completely replaced the biodegradable tube with a matrix of natural collagen identical to a patient's own – except thicker and better able to withstand the extra pressures of dialysis. After decellularisation, these tubes were surgically implanted. Niklason's vein matrices

have been plumbed into the arms of 60 volunteers in Europe and the US and served as the vein for dialysis. The grafts can be used within eight weeks, and after several months, they were still going strong.

That said, artificial matrix still does not have the myriad properties of natural matrix. Sumitran-Holgersson, who has worked with artificial materials at Gothenberg University, says that despite the potential for synthetic implants, natural matrices will always be crucial for building organs. "It's definitely superior because it retains so many important factors to bind and differentiate the cells," she says.

For some applications, however, it has been possible to create hybrids that couple the best of both worlds. This provides a promising avenue to treat one of the worst consequences of Crohn's disease: peri-anal fistulas.

These abscesses eat a channel through the bowel which allows faecal matter to seep out

"The biodegradable implant was soon replaced by a matrix of natural collagen identical to the patient's"

Surgery's new sound

Some invasive surgeries are becoming a thing of the past, thanks to a clever way of focusing acoustic waves, finds Helen Thomson

PHYLLIS is having brain surgery. But she is wide awake. There are no scalpels and no blood, sliced flesh or bone in sight. Instead, the surgeon carefully places a cap on top of Phyllis's head and flicks a switch. Deep inside her brain, a tiny region of tissue heats up and begins to burn, while surrounding brain cells are left unscathed. Later that day, Phyllis is able to go home, free from the neurological disorder that for the past 30 years has made her right hand tremble violently whenever she tried to use it.

She has a form of ultrasound to thank for her remarkable recovery. Just as the sun's rays can be focused by a magnifying glass to burn a piece of paper, high-intensity ultrasound waves can be concentrated to burn human tissue. The waves are harmless until they converge at the focal point, so a surgeon can operate deep inside the body without harming the surrounding tissue.

This high-intensity focused ultrasound (HIFU) requires no cuts to be made, and many operations don't even need an anaesthetic, so the patient can be in and out of hospital within a day. "When you're dealing with a lot of very sick people, that's a huge advantage," says Gail ter Haar, who studies ultrasound at the Institute of Cancer Research in London.

After promising trials treating prostate cancer, it is now looking as if HIFU could become a medical Swiss army knife for all kinds of procedures. And even in parts of the body where the focused waves can't burn away tissue directly, they can still boost the uptake of drugs in specific organs. The method has even been used to prevent severe illness in fetuses in the womb.

Phyllis's success story is the latest step of a journey that began 70 years ago. John Lynn and his colleagues at Columbia University in New York were the first to try targeting ultrasound waves to destroy biological tissue, in the 1940s. Although they managed to create lesions in cat brains with minimal disruption to non-targeted areas, the need for a craniotomy – in which a bone flap is removed from the skull – together with a lack of sophisticated imaging technologies meant there was limited interest in the technology for general surgery. Now, with more advanced transmitters that can focus beams behind hard tissue like bone, and imaging technology such as MRI, doctors can operate more accurately, targeting areas of tissue sometimes just fractions of a millimetre across.

That precision looks set to revolutionise the treatment of prostate cancer. Conventionally, when tumours need to be eliminated, the entire prostate is removed, which can damage nerves and the muscles that control the ability to relieve yourself on demand. The result is that 70 per cent of patients lose the ability to get erections, and about 15 per cent become incontinent. A less invasive option is radiotherapy, but it can still cause some damage to surrounding nerves. What's more, radiotherapy is unlikely to be repeated if the cancer returns, because the risk becomes too great that DNA damage from the radiation will cause secondary tumours.

With focused ultrasound, however, surgeons can burn away tumours bit by bit, targeting areas the size of a grain of rice (see "No blood, sweat or tears", page 88). Trial results so far have been impressive: in a 2012 study of about 40 men receiving HIFU, 90 per cent could maintain an erection by the end of the study, and no man was left incontinent. One year later, 95 per cent showed no signs of the disease.

The recovery times are particularly notable. "We've had some people who've said they've been shopping the same day as the procedure," says Louise Dickinson at University College London Hospitals, who is investigating the long-term outcomes of using the therapy ❯

for prostate cancer. "One man said it was easier than going to the dentist for a filling." Widespread clinical trials of ultrasound treatment for prostate cancer are now under way, but further evidence of its long-term effectiveness will be needed before it is a recommended treatment.

Buoyed by the promising results for prostate cancer, a range of trials are now investigating using sound to treat other disorders, including pancreatic cancer and lumps that form in the thyroid gland that can lead to cancer. One of the more ambitious ideas is to use HIFU to tackle problems deep in the brain. The technique has huge advantages, not least because you avoid cracking into the skull. What's more, you can bypass the healthy layers of brain, preserving normal functions.

That's not to say it is simple. The rate at which ultrasound passes through different tissue types varies – bone absorbs a lot of sound, whereas the jelly-like tissue of the brain takes in much less. To make matters worse, our

"There was a strange buzzing sensation, but the brain surgery was completely painless"

skulls are not a uniform thickness all the way around. So surgeons have to use CAT scans to measure the bone density at thousands of points around the scalp. Later, a cap full of ultrasound emitters, called transducers, will be placed on the patient's head. Each transducer is tuned using information about the bone density underneath so that it emits just the right frequency, for just the right amount of time, to focus the waves at the desired point in the brain.

In 2013, the technique was used to treat 15 people with essential tremor, Phyllis among them. To do so, the doctors singed a tiny area of the thalamus that relays motor signals to the cortex – thus blocking some of the

NO BLOOD, SWEAT OR TEARS

I'm in scrubs, hairnet in place. The surgical theatre is cool, with music playing softly in the background. Nurses are busy preparing equipment. Caroline Moore - a surgeon at University College London Hospitals - is busy double-checking some scans. So far, so ER.

But one thing is missing. Although the patient lying in front of me is fully anaesthetised and about to have his prostate cancer treated, there are no needles, scissors or scalpels in sight.

Instead, Moore gently inserts a high-intensity focused ultrasound (HIFU) probe into the patient's rectum. She sits between his legs and boots up a programme on a computer screen. She asks for the lights to be dimmed.

A low-intensity beam of ultrasound produces a scan of the patient's prostate, which appears on Moore's screen. She adjusts the probe to get a better view - having already analysed previous MRI and biopsy results from the patient, she knows exactly where his tumours are.

Using the real-time scans provided by the probe, Moore marks on the screen which areas of the prostate need destroying. She checks her measurements from several angles. Then she presses "start".

You wouldn't know anything had happened. The regular beep, beep, beep

of the patient's heartbeat breaks the silence, but other than that, the theatre is dark and uneventful.

Inside the patient, it's a different story. The probe is now emitting a regular burst of focused ultrasound energy on to the areas previously dictated by Moore on the computer screen. This heats up tiny areas of the prostate for 3 seconds. The probe stops emitting ultrasound for 6 seconds and then starts again. The heat created by the energy destroys the tumour.

Although the patient's surgery is now under the control of a computer, Moore still has a lot to do. As the prostate heats up and tissue is destroyed, swelling occurs. She continuously compares real-time scans with the patient's first scan so she can counteract movement of the probe caused by any swelling. Occasionally the prostate gets too hot and she presses the pause button.

Moore's patient will leave hospital later that afternoon. He has to put up with a catheter for a week, but hopefully he is now cancer-free. There's also a good chance he will have kept his ability to maintain erections without pills, says Moore, and there's a less than 1 per cent chance of him becoming incontinent. "No surgery is completely side-effect free," says Moore, "but we're getting closer with HIFU."

abnormal neuronal activity that would otherwise be transmitted to the muscles and cause shaking. "The whole procedure probably took less than 2 hours, and apart from a strange buzzing sensation, it was completely painless," says Phyllis. Because the trial was designed to test the safety of the procedure, they only aimed to treat the movements in her right hand. The results were immediate. "As soon as I came out of hospital, my handwriting was perfect, like it used to be," she says. "It's got a little worse over time but it's so much better than my left hand." The other 14 patients in the trial experienced similar improvements, and although side effects

almost untouchable, because skeletal tissue quickly absorbs the ultrasound waves. "It's hard to get any energy deep into the bone," says Wladyslaw Gedroyc, a consultant radiologist at St Mary's Hospital in London. Conventional surgery, too, struggles to remove this kind of cancer, because it is difficult to bypass vital nerves and any bone that is removed has to be reconstructed with a graft or prosthesis.

Bursting bubbles

Focused ultrasound may be much more than a replacement for the scalpel, however. It could open doors to procedures that would be impossible by conventional methods. Of particular interest is using ultrasound to direct the delivery of drugs. One approach would be to create medicines that are injected in an inert form, and then activated near to a tumour using heat from HIFU. The idea is to boost the dose where it is most needed while reducing side effects in the rest of the body.

In other instances, the treatment could be aided by "microbubbles". This phenomenon was discovered by accident, or so the legend goes, says Eleanor Stride at the University of Oxford. "They used to be made just by shaking blood about and putting it back in." Now, you can buy ready-made microbubbles that are between 1 and 10 micrometres across. They are comprised of a bubble filled with gas, supported by an outer shell made of lipids, proteins or polymers. The bubbles are often used during ultrasound scans, since they increase the contrast of the blood supply compared with the surrounding tissue. Once they are placed in the path of an ultrasound wave of the right frequency and intensity, however, they expand and contract until they suddenly collapse, creating a shockwave.

Do this in the brain, and you could perforate the blood-brain barrier – the layer of membranes around capillaries that separate the blood from the extracellular fluid that flows around the brain. This barrier makes it difficult to deliver drugs into the brain during chemotherapy, for instance – but puncturing it is a tricky procedure, because permanent damage would weaken the brain's defences against bacteria. A 2012 study in macaques, however, identified the specific frequency necessary to induce a reversible disruption to this barrier for just a few hours – enough time to allow drugs to be delivered to the brain with a minimal risk of infection.

Elsewhere in the body, it might be possible to place traditional chemotherapy agents into microbubbles and direct their implosion at

the site you want destroyed. "It's not been done yet, but we're getting very close," says Stride. Her colleague Constantin Coussios has taken the first step, by starting a trial in which people with liver cancer receive a chemotherapy drug encased in a lipid wrapper that can be broken down using ultrasound. The first person was treated successfully in early 2015. If all goes well, they will then try to use microbubbles, filled with gas and the drug, as a vehicle – with the added advantage that the shockwave of the imploding bubbles would drive its chemical load deeper into the tumour, where it can do more damage (see also "Panacea", page 34). A similar approach would be particularly useful to push drugs into the bone cancers that are so difficult to reach with traditional surgery.

Focused sound can even help doctors to treat patients at times when they were thought to be untouchable – such as when they are still in the womb. This was demonstrated for the first time in 2013, with a condition known as "twin

"The shockwave of the collapsing bubbles pushes the drugs deeper into the tumour"

reversed arterial perfusion". This rare disorder involves two fetuses – one of which develops normally, while the other fails to develop a head, arms or heart. The two fetuses are connected by an umbilical cord that passes through the placenta, and the twin without a heart relies on blood pumped from its twin to stay alive. As a result, the healthy twin has to work extra hard to sustain both, which often results in heart failure and death.

Surgeons used HIFU, between 13 and 17 weeks after conception, to sever the abnormal fetus from the placenta and release the healthy twin of this burden. The baby boy was later delivered successfully (see also "Healed in the womb", page 68).

The success of such a delicate procedure offers a glimpse of what the future might hold. Neal Kassell, director of the Focused Ultrasound Foundation, says we are only just beginning to understand the potential of this technology. "It's a stick that we're still working out how to wield," he says.

Gedroyc agrees. "You have here a very powerful tool," he says. "Once you start thinking about it, you're really only limited by how imaginative you are." ∎

included temporary problems with speech, and for four patients, minor but persistent alterations to sensations in their face or fingers, all agreed that it significantly improved their quality of life.

The hope is that we might be on the cusp of a new wave of non-invasive brain surgery. The Focused Ultrasound Foundation in Charlottesville, Virginia, which was set up to help develop ultrasound therapy, has now begun clinical trials investigating the use of HIFU to treat movement problems in Parkinson's and other disorders.

Despite these successes, HIFU has its limitations. Bone cancer, for instance, is

Could high-tech intensive care medicine be doing more harm than good? **Dan Jones** finds out

Darwin's doctor

NOTHING epitomises cutting-edge medicine so much as a modern intensive care unit. Among the serried ranks of shiny chrome and plastic surrounding each bed are machines to ventilate the lungs and keep failing kidneys functioning, devices to deliver drugs intravenously and supply sedatives, tubes to get food into a patient and waste out, and countless gizmos to monitor blood composition, heart rate, pulse and other physiological indicators.

This environment is home to Mervyn Singer, who specialises in intensive care medicine at University College London. So you might expect him to wax lyrical about the wonders of medical technology. Instead, he has this to say of recent advances: "Virtually all have involved doing less to the patient." And he goes further, arguing provocatively that modern critical care interferes with the body's natural protective mechanisms – that patients often survive in spite of medical interventions rather than because of them.

It is a counter-intuitive idea, to say the least,

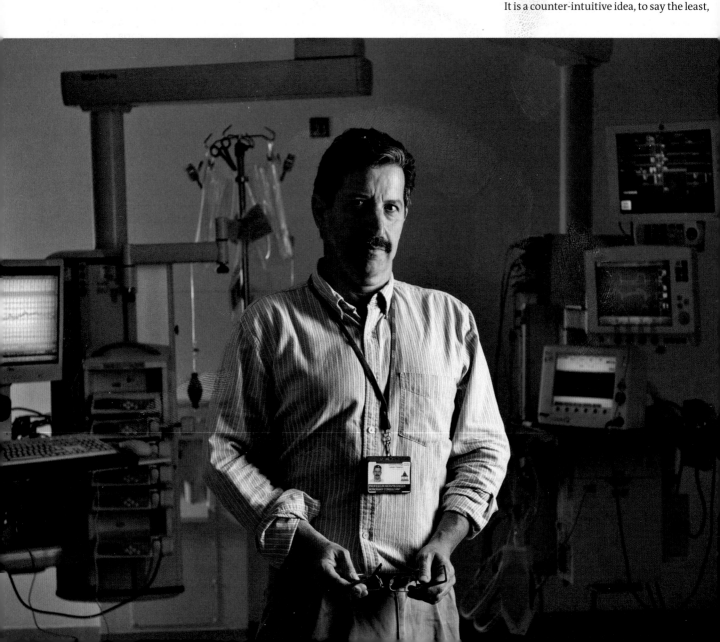

yet there is an underlying logic. Taking an evolutionary perspective, Singer points out that the human body is adapted to deal with the types of threats to which our ancestors were exposed, and those include critical illness. Our immune system can fight off infections, our blood clots so that we don't bleed to death with every cut, tissues regenerate and bone fractures heal, if imperfectly, over time. "We have evolved to deal with temperature extremes, starvation, trauma and infection," says Singer. "We haven't evolved to cope with being sedated, put on a ventilator and pumped full of drugs."

Such Darwinian thinking about health and illness is not new, but it is not a part of mainstream medicine or intensive care. "The application of evolutionary thinking in critical care medicine has been surprisingly lacking," says Randolph Nesse, a pioneer of Darwinian medicine and director of the Center for Evolution and Medicine at Arizona State University. "Much of critical care medicine is based on a tacit theory that is rarely examined – namely, that almost all of the changes seen in severe illness are pathological." Singer's approach holds this assumption up to scrutiny, and asks whether the changes are actually coping strategies, meaning that modern medicine might be interfering with the body's natural protective mechanisms.

Patients can end up in an intensive care unit for many reasons: they may have survived an accident, succumbed to a serious infection or undergone major surgery. Yet, once there, their condition often follows a similar clinical path. Both trauma and infection elicit a strong local inflammatory immune response at the site of injury or infection. This helps fend off microorganisms that might enter the body, and also rallies immune cells to break down damaged tissue. Although these responses cause local tissue damage prior to healing, they protect the body as a whole.

In severe cases, however, a localised reaction can become a body-wide systemic inflammatory response syndrome (SIRS). If infection is the trigger, this response is called sepsis. In the first "acute" stage, the immune system ramps up its activity, stress hormones are released and metabolism increases. Patients typically experience abnormal body temperature, a high heart rate and increased breathing. They may then recover, but in many patients severe inflammation progresses over a period of hours or days and begins to affect the normal functioning of the body's organs. If equilibrium cannot be restored, multiple organ failure can set in. This is the leading cause of death for critically ill patients in ICUs, accounting for more than

two-thirds of deaths after the first week. The initial trauma often involves blood loss, and severe vomiting and diarrhoea. Later, the overblown inflammatory response can cause fluid to leak out of the circulation. This fluid loss means less oxygen reaches organs, causing cells to die. That, at least, is the accepted view. Singer is not convinced.

He points to evidence from post-mortem studies on patients who have died after multiple organ failure, whose organs in fact look normal, with little sign of damage from a lack of oxygen. And where patients survive, normal function is rapidly restored, even in organs with little capacity for regeneration. After acute kidney failure, for example, only 1 per cent of people need lifelong dialysis. There is also evidence that during the "multiple organ dysfunction" phase of sepsis and SIRS, oxygen still reaches the organs – they just use less of it for metabolism.

Singer concludes that organs do not fail so much as shut down in an adaptive response to the extreme stress of critical illness. His interpretation of the process goes as follows: during the first hours and days after major trauma or infection, the body enters an inflammatory "fight mode", burning energy and pumping out stress hormones such as adrenaline and cortisol, as well as chemicals that modulate the immune response. If this doesn't work, metabolism starts to drop, triggered by a decrease in energy production by the mitochondria, the cell's powerhouses. This happens because the hormones and immune chemicals inhibit and damage mitochondria, and changes in gene expression limit the production of new ones. Under these conditions, attempts to maintain normal functioning can trigger cell death. To avoid this fate, cells switch to a dormant state, causing organs to shut down.

We have unrecognised ways of coping with critical illness, according to Mervyn Singer

In this view, multiple organ dysfunction is a strategic and temporary change, comparable to hibernation or torpor. Far from being a catastrophic development that must be mitigated at all costs, it is the body's ultimate rescue attempt. By slowing metabolism right down, organs have a better chance of resuming normal function, if and when the critical

"The human body is adapted to deal with the types of threats to which our ancestors were exposed"

illness passes. It's a risky strategy, but then desperate times call for desperate measures.

Singer's thesis isn't just a novel way of interpreting multiple organ failure. It could also explain one of the big mysteries of intensive care – why many drugs and interventions have been linked to worse outcomes. For example, certain types of antibiotics and sedatives damp down energy production by mitochondria, so if given early they might interfere with the high-energy requirements of the acute phase of critical illness. What's more, antibiotics and sedatives interfere with immune functioning and can also cause problems for patients who survive organ shutdown and need to re-establish normal metabolism. This is because the drugs keep energy production low and also prevent the formation of new mitochondria to replace those lost during organ shutdown.

Singer published the definitive statement of his hypothesis in 2009. The following year, he presented the idea at a conference entitled Evolutionary Approaches to Disease and Health, where it generated considerable interest among an audience of evolutionary-minded researchers. "Singer's work is a fine example of the value of evolutionary thinking in medicine," said Nesse, who was at the meeting. He has long campaigned for trainee doctors to be taught evolutionary biology as a foundation for understanding what the human body is and how it works.

Intensive care specialists are also open to Singer's views, if only to invigorate the discipline. "Although we've tried hard over the past 40 years to improve patient outcomes, mortality rates have dropped only slightly," says Falco Hietbrink, at the University Medical Center in Utrecht, the Netherlands. Nevertheless, some clinicians will require more convincing. "I love imaginative hypotheses, and this is a fascinating possibility," says Luciano Gattinoni of the Institute of Anaesthesia and Intensive Care at Ospedale Maggiore Policlinico in Milan, Italy. However, he points out that there is scant autopsy evidence on whether multiple organ dysfunction causes cell death or serves a

Failure or strategic shutdown?

It has been assumed that the body's acute response following trauma leads to a lack of oxygen and cell death, but according to Mervyn Singer's theory, the body's first response is a "fight mode", followed by a "shutdown" stage that is a last ditch attempt at preservation

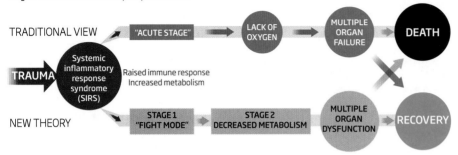

TRADITIONAL VIEW → "ACUTE STAGE" → LACK OF OXYGEN → MULTIPLE ORGAN FAILURE → DEATH

TRAUMA → Systemic inflammatory response syndrome (SIRS) — Raised immune response / Increased metabolism

NEW THEORY → STAGE 1 "FIGHT MODE" → STAGE 2 DECREASED METABOLISM → MULTIPLE ORGAN DYSFUNCTION → RECOVERY

BATTLE HARDENED

Records from historical battles provide evidence for the remarkable capacity of the human body to cope with massive trauma. The Battle of Trafalgar, which took place on 21 October 1805, was a particularly bloody affair: by the end of the day there were more than 450 British fatalities, while the Spanish and French forces suffered the loss of more than 3200 soldiers. Thousands more were wounded. William Beatty, the physician on the British flagship HMS Victory, recorded 102 wounded soldiers on board. Despite having none of the medical technology available to today's intensive care patients and performing 10 amputations, only six of the wounded subsequently died of their injuries.

Ten years later, a similarly high survival rate was recorded among the 13th Light Dragoons in the Battle of Waterloo. Only three of the 52 wounded soldiers later died of their wounds.

Medical records from the American civil war between 1861 and 1865 tell the same story. Approximately 15 per cent of all mortalities occurred on the battlefield, with around twice as many soldiers dying from diseases as a result of poor sanitation and living conditions.

Amputation was the main treatment for injuries, with surgeons working around the clock to remove limbs and digits. Operations often took no more than 10 minutes and, with little water available, hands and instruments went unwashed between procedures. Despite all this around three-quarters of amputees survived.

LESS IS MORE

Intensive care medicine is only about 50 years old. In the early days the logic of treatment seemed commonsensical. "We thought, 'antibiotics are good, so more antibiotics are better. Breathing is good, so more air is better'," says Luciano Gattinoni at Ospedale Maggiore Policlinico in Milan, Italy. "We were doing the right things conceptually, but exaggerating everything."

Nowadays, the trend is for less intervention, not more. Perhaps the biggest advance in recent years has been in the way patients are mechanically ventilated.

Pumping air into the lungs can damage them, because they are normally inflated by inhalation, in which negative pressure draws in air. By reducing the volume of air pumped in each breath cycle and increasing the frequency of artificial breaths, mechanical ventilation has become much more successful.

Doctors also recognise that even essential interventions can cause problems. Entry points for tubes can become infected, which can prove fatal for patients in a weakened state. Sedatives have been linked to poor patient outcomes in some studies.

Working on the assumption that intensive care should support patients while not adding to the stress that their bodies are under, the idea that less is more is increasingly mainstream.

protective role. "Really, we don't have enough data to settle these questions, which is quite surprising."

Another obvious criticism of the idea that multiple organ dysfunction is adaptive is that it is not tremendously successful as a survival strategy. Not only is organ failure a principal cause of death among people in intensive care, but the more organs that fail, the more likely a patient is to die. And among patients who survive, the severity of multiple organ failure correlates with quality of life in the long term.

Singer acknowledges that, at best, it is only a partially successful strategy – though one that may allow the hardy to survive to fight another day, an obvious evolutionary advantage. In fact, he is impressed by how effective it is, given that it is a last-ditch response. Witness the high survival rates of injured soldiers in the days before modern medicine (see "Battle hardened", left).

Reconsidering the options

The key issue, of course, is what all this means for treatment. "If some aspects of the condition are adaptive, then clinicians should work with them, not against them," says Singer. For starters, doctors might want to reconsider the doses and course durations of antibiotics and sedatives. Likewise for interventions designed to enhance oxygen delivery to tissues. These may prove beneficial when given early, but could be ineffective or even harmful later on if the extra oxygen bumps up metabolic activity that cannot be supported by the mitochondria and so leads to cell death. And critically ill people might benefit from the timely administration of therapies that protect mitochondrial function, such as antioxidants. Likewise treatments that stimulate the production of new mitochondria, including hormones like oestrogen and the gas nitric oxide.

The precise therapeutic implications of rethinking organ dysfunction will depend on acquiring clinical evidence about what works and what does not. "Evolutionary medicine does not prescribe what treatment is best," says Nesse. "[It] suggests what we should think about and what studies we should do." But if the upshot is that intensive care becomes less intensive that might not actually be so revolutionary (see "Less is more", left).

Singer may not be correct in every detail, but in the long run being provocative could be more important than being right. "Singer will get people thinking in new ways," says Nesse. In terms of improving the care of critically ill patients, that's got to be what the doctor ordered. ∎

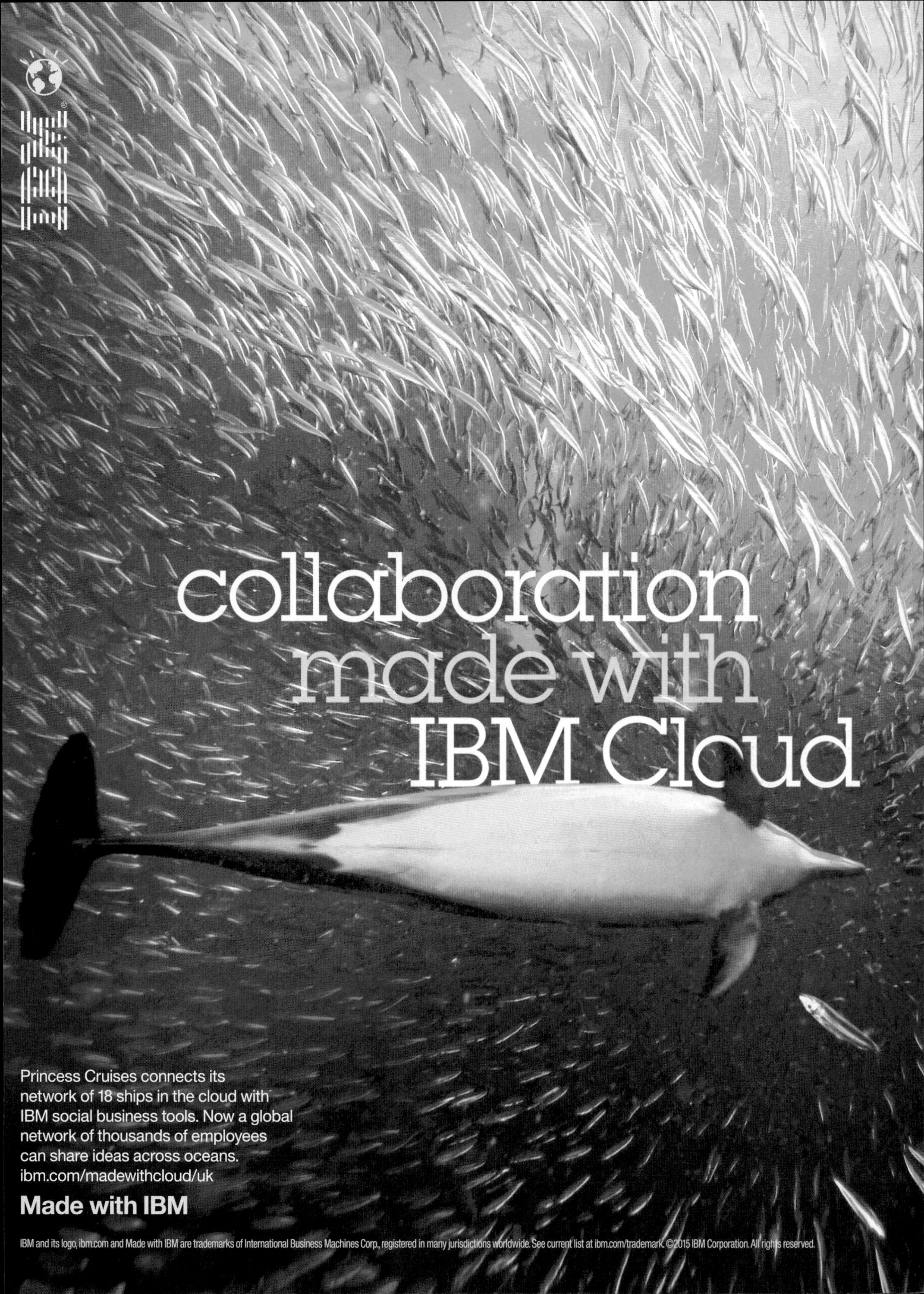

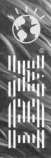

collaboration
made with
IBM Cloud
Princess Cruises connects its network of 18 ships in the cloud with IBM social business tools. Now a global network of thousands of employees can share ideas across oceans.
ibm.com/madewithcloud/uk
Made with IBM
IBM and its logo, ibm.com and Made with IBM are trademarks of International Business Machines Corp., registered in many jurisdictions worldwide. See current list at ibm.com/trademark. ©2015 IBM Corporation. All rights reserved.

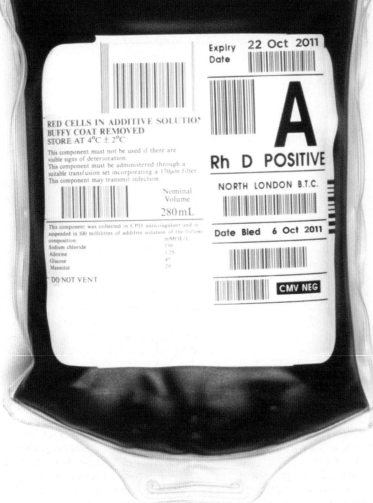

RED CELLS IN ADDITIVE SOLUTION
BUFFY COAT REMOVED
STORE AT 4°C ± 2°C

This component must not be used if there are
visible signs of deterioration.
This component must be administered through a
suitable transfusion set incorporating a 170μm filter.
This component may transmit infection.

Nominal
Volume

280 mL

This component was collected in CPD anticoagulant and is
suspended in 100 millilitres of additive solution of the following
composition: mMOL/L
Sodium chloride   150
Adenine   1.25
Glucose   45
Mannitol   29

DO NOT VENT

Expiry   22 Oct 2011
Date

A
Rh D POSITIVE

NORTH LONDON B.T.C.

Date Bled   6 Oct 2011

CMV NEG

Code RED

If you get hit by a truck, fixing
your body should take second
place to fixing your blood.
David Cohen reports

Your chances
of surviving massive
blood loss are 50:50

SKIMMING over the London rooftops, the air ambulance takes only minutes to arrive. Its objective: a cyclist who has been hit by a truck. Her pelvis has been crushed and she is haemorrhaging internally from her liver and kidneys. As her blood pressure plummets, the patient goes into medical shock. She is dying.

But the paramedics do not give fluids to boost blood pressure and reverse the shock as they normally would. Instead, they begin a set of radically different last-ditch procedures. The patient is anaesthetised and rushed by helicopter to the Royal London Hospital. Over the radio the crew warn the hospital's waiting trauma team about the patient's state: "Code red."

The approach has arisen because of discoveries made in recent years about what happens in the chaos of major haemorrhage. Doctors have found that some people can bleed to death even after reaching hospital, because their blood simply fails to clot as it should.

"Every stitch you make bleeds, they start bleeding from the punctures at the site of their infusions, everything you do causes bleeding," says Karim Brohi, a trauma surgeon at the Royal London Hospital. "They bleed from their mouth and nose, and into their lungs, so they start to drown in their own fluids. You're filled with an impending sense of doom. You just know the patient is going to die."

It seems that sometimes major injuries trigger a problem with the blood-clotting process, causing blood to leak from the body faster than it can be stemmed. This clotting disorder affects as many as 1 in 4 major trauma victims. So Brohi and others have developed a way of treating people that prioritises fixing their blood over fixing their body. It's a radical departure from standard procedures, but it could save thousands of lives every year worldwide.

Key to the switch is a new understanding of coagulation: the mysterious, almost magical, process whereby blood changes from a fluid into a solid to form a clot. Coagulation is regulated by a complex network of blood-borne proteins which ensure that the process is triggered as soon as it is needed and yet only when it is needed; unwanted clots can be lethal in their own right.

Normally, the blood's viscosity is finely poised. If you cut yourself, blood proteins known as clotting factors trigger coagulation. The end result is a plug made of a stringy protein called fibrin, and tiny cell fragments called platelets. Meanwhile, further from the

MAIN: JANE STOCKMAN /GETTY; LEFT: DAVID LEVENE/EYEVINE

"They bleed from their mouth and into their lungs so they start to drown in their own fluids. You just know they are going to die"

damage, anticoagulants are made that stop the clotting process from spreading too far.

Some people are born with a blood-clotting disorder, or coagulopathy. Blood may fail to clot when it should, such as in people with haemophilia, or it can be too prone to clotting and trigger a stroke. But any one of us who is injured badly enough can experience acute traumatic coagulopathy (ATC), as Brohi discovered some years ago.

Clotting switch

Brohi admits he stumbled on ATC almost by accident in 2000 when he decided to study severe trauma patients who had been admitted to hospital. "We were doing an exhaustive search to understand what the data said about patients' clotting ability early after trauma, but we weren't expecting to find anything," he says.

People who bleed heavily were already known to develop some kind of clotting disorder, but it was thought this only became

a problem after they had been in hospital for some time, possibly hours after arrival. The problem was thought to result from their deteriorating condition, perhaps exacerbated by the fluids given to raise their blood pressure, which have the unwanted effect of diluting levels of clotting factors.

Brohi analysed the records of more than 1000 patients and, to his surprise, found they often had the clotting disorder on arrival at hospital. It seemed to arise within minutes of injury, as a direct consequence of massive tissue damage. What's more, 46 per cent of those who had the disorder on admission died, compared with 11 per cent of those who did not.

The results flew in the face of conventional wisdom. "We had a lot of difficulty publishing the paper at first," says Brohi. But a few months later, a study of 20,000 patients in a hospital in Miami showed the same thing, and many studies since have confirmed the finding.

Since then Brohi and his colleagues, along with other research teams around the ➤

Blood bath

Major physical injuries can trigger a breakdown of the normal clotting process, causing blood to leak from the body faster than it can be stemmed

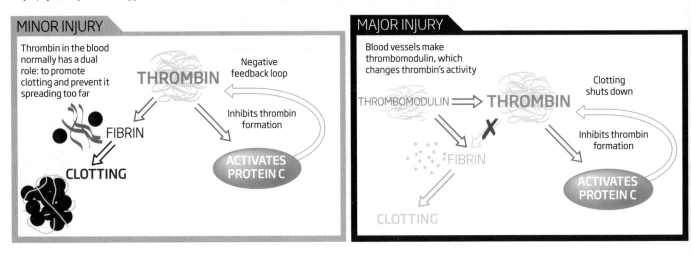

MINOR INJURY

Thrombin in the blood normally has a dual role: to promote clotting and prevent it spreading too far

THROMBIN

Negative feedback loop

Inhibits thrombin formation

FIBRIN

ACTIVATES PROTEIN C

CLOTTING

MAJOR INJURY

Blood vessels make thrombomodulin, which changes thrombin's activity

THROMBOMODULIN → THROMBIN

Clotting shuts down

Inhibits thrombin formation

FIBRIN

ACTIVATES PROTEIN C

CLOTTING

---

world, have focused on unpicking the causes of ATC. Normally an enzyme called thrombin is a key driver of fibrin formation. To put the brakes on the coagulation process there is a clever feedback loop: thrombin also activates a compound called protein C, which blocks thrombin formation (see diagram).

In someone experiencing ATC, however, cells on the inner surface of blood vessels begin to make a protein called thrombomodulin – not just at the site of injury, but throughout the body. Thrombomodulin switches thrombin from its primary role of forming clots to its other role of activating protein C, leading to a wave of anticoagulant proteins washing through the body. This "thrombin switch" is why people with ATC bleed so profusely.

So what prompts blood vessels to make thrombomodulin? It seems to be severe physical injury combined with the person going into medical shock, which happens when the tissues of the body do not get enough oxygen. "We don't understand why these factors are crucial, but you don't get ATC without both," says Brohi.

It is unclear why big injuries lead to the production of thrombomodulin throughout the body, but from an evolutionary perspective it is not that surprising. Clotting has evolved to deal with small, survivable injuries like cuts and grazes. "Getting hit by a bus is not something we've developed an evolutionary response to," says Brohi. After such an extreme injury, our finely tuned system breaks down.

The existence of ATC is now widely accepted, but what to do about it is still contentious. As yet there is no drug that

"Clotting has evolved to deal with small survivable injuries. It can't deal with getting hit by a bus"

specifically reverses the condition, although several groups are trying to develop one.

In the meantime, a growing number of doctors are trying to save people by using existing drugs and techniques differently, under a protocol termed damage control resuscitation. It's a switch in priorities: tackling the clotting disorder takes precedence over repairing injuries. "It is a huge change in mindset," says Brohi.

Blood-chilling

Take the cyclist hit by the truck. Previously, paramedics would have immediately given her a large saline infusion to bring up her blood pressure, and so help blood and therefore oxygen return to her tissues.

At the Royal London Hospital, however, the priority is to maintain clotting at all costs for anyone at risk of ATC. So saline is out for several reasons. It would dilute the blood's clotting factors and, as it is stored below body temperature, would chill the blood, which also slows coagulation. What's more, the pushing, pulsing force of blood at higher pressure makes it harder for clots to form, so we want to keep pressure low anyway.

Patients also get different blood products. These days there's no such thing as a plain "blood transfusion"; for many decades, donated blood has been separated into its three constituents – red blood cells, platelets and plasma, the straw-coloured fluid component of blood. It makes storage easier, and giving people different cocktails of these components according to their needs is a better way to husband supplies.

Until recently, people bleeding profusely were given mainly red blood cells with small amounts of plasma and platelets, typically in a ratio of 8:1:1. The lack of oxygen-carrying red blood cells was seen as the most immediate threat to life.

But plasma contains the blood's clotting factors and platelets are, after all, a structural component of the clot. "We were giving patients blood without clotting factors in it," says Bryan Cotton, a surgeon at the University of Texas, Houston, who has investigated the best ratios to use.

Under damage control protocols, people get higher doses of plasma and platelets in a 1:1:1 ratio. As fast as possible, they also get extra clotting factors and a drug called tranexamic acid that inhibits clot breakdown.

Road traffic accidents are the biggest cause of death for young people

The largest such trial to date, by a US team that included Cotton, was published in 2015 and compared ratios of 1:1:1 and 2:1:1. The researchers found no significant difference in mortality overall, but patients on the 1:1:1 ratio were less likely to bleed to death and had higher rates of successful blood clotting.

Some doctors have raised concerns about giving more plasma, because the more blood products people are given, the higher the risk of organ failure and infection, so they should only be used if essential. But that might not necessarily be an issue. At Cotton's hospital, which adopted damage control procedures, doctors found that giving more plasma early on reduced the need for it during later medical care. "We have decreased the amount of plasma used at the hospital," says Cotton.

There may be a way to work out who needs plasma the most, with a device called a thromboelastometer, currently used to test blood in people with other clotting disorders. It vibrates a needle in a small sample of blood, and as the blood begins to clot, resistance to the vibration increases. Normal blood thickens like custard within minutes, but blood from someone with ATC can take much longer. "You can tell within about 5 minutes whether the patient has ATC," says Brohi. Other tests can take over an hour.

How about comparing hospitals that follow damage control protocols with those that don't? Brohi published a study on this in 2010, and he says the figures speak for themselves. "If you come to our hospital injured, bleeding and shocked, you are three times more likely to survive than at any other trauma centre in the UK," he said at the time.

But the Royal London is one of the world's top trauma centres, so there may have been many factors contributing to those figures. "Certain things may happen on the way to hospital or in intensive care that set the outcome, regardless of the quality of the transfusions," says Thomas Scalea, physician-in-chief at the University of Maryland Medical Center in Baltimore, who was involved in the blood ratio trial.

"In the end we have to prove it at the bedside," he says. "It's important science, but if it doesn't translate into improved outcomes then it's just science. If it translates, then it is revolutionary."

And the cyclist? Her ordeal was by no means over; she needed several further rounds of reconstructive surgery. Two months after the crash, she had to learn how to walk again, and suffers chronic back pain.

But she is alive. ∎

"We send blood products up to the helipad if necessary," says Brohi.

Another crucial element is a switch to what's called damage control surgery, which means doing the minimum work needed to stem the major sources of blood loss, before sending the patient to intensive care where they can be stabilised. Later they can have the more time-consuming reconstructive surgery.

The concept has been around for decades but until now has not been used often. What's new is to use this approach routinely on anyone with possible ATC.

That's what happened with the cyclist. When she reached the operating theatre, the surgeons limited themselves to repairing damaged organs and major blood vessels. Within 25 minutes she was whisked to intensive care to get more blood and extra clotting factors. Only once she was clotting well was her blood pressure returned to normal. Then she was sent back to theatre for further surgery on her pelvis.

The number of hospitals using damage control procedures is steadily growing. Even so, randomised trials comparing the approach with standard practice have been lacking – even in animals. Unlike a new drug or medical device, there is no such requirement for a new surgical technique or a change in the way existing drugs are used.

Individual elements of the approach have come under scrutiny, though. For instance, several studies have supported the idea of giving tranexamic acid, and using less saline than is standard practice.

Thickening like custard

When it comes to blood ratios, the approach has started to change. Most protocols now recommend ratios of at least 2:1 for red blood cells and plasma, though the exact ratio for platelet transfusions is still unclear, Brohi says. Some studies have found 1:1:1 is best, and this ratio is now frequently used.

One of the difficulties with deciding on the ratios to use is that most studies are retrospective. In other words, they look at historical data on what blood products people got and whether they lived or died. There could have been other factors making those who were in better shape more likely to get 1:1:1, for instance. What are needed are prospective trials, where people are randomised to different ratios in advance.

Resurrection man

Resuscitation specialist **Sam Parnia** believes we can bring many more people back to life after they die – it's just a matter of training and equipment. He also tells **Dick Teresi** why he is investigating what happens to consciousness after death

Are the people you resuscitate after cardiac arrest really dead? Isn't the definition of death that it is irreversible?
A cardiac arrest is the same as death. It's just semantics. After a gunshot wound, if the person haemorrhages sufficiently, then the heart stops beating and they die. The social perception of death is that you have reached a point from which you can never come back, but medically speaking, death is a biological process. For millennia we have considered someone dead when their heart stops beating.

People often confuse the terms cardiac arrest and heart attack. Clearly, they're very different.
A heart attack happens when a clot blocks a blood vessel to the heart. The portion of the heart muscle that was supplied blood and oxygen by that vessel will then die. That's why most people with a heart attack don't die.

What is the biggest problem in bringing someone back to life?
Reversing death before the person has too much cell damage. People die under many different circumstances and under the watch of many different medical specialists. No single speciality is charged with taking and implementing all the latest advances and technology in resuscitation.

How long after they die can someone still be resuscitated?
People have been resuscitated four or five hours after death – after basically lying there as a corpse. Once we die the cells in the body undergo their own process of death. After eight hours it's impossible to bring the brain cells back.

What is the best way to bring people back?
The ideal system – and they do this a lot in

South-East Asia, Japan and South Korea – is called ECPR. The E stands for extra corporeal membrane oxygenation (ECMO). It's a system in which you take blood from a person who has had a cardiac arrest, and circulate it through a membrane oxygenator, which supplies oxygen and removes carbon dioxide. Then you pump the blood back into circulation around the body. Using ECMO, they have brought people back five to seven hours after they died. ECMO is not routinely available in the US and UK, though.

So, when I go into cardiac arrest, ideally what steps do I want my doctors to take?
First, we start the patient on a machine that provides chest compressions and breathing. Then we attach the patient to a monitor that tells us the quality of oxygen that's getting into the brain.

If we do the chest compressions and breathing and give the right drugs and we still can't get the oxygen levels to normal, then we go to ECMO. This system can restore normal oxygen levels in the brain and deliver the right amount of oxygen to all the organs to minimise injury.

At the same time you also cool the patient. This slows the rate of metabolic activity in the brain cells to halt the process of cell death while you go and fix the underlying problem.

How do you cool the body?
It used to be ice packs. Today a whole industry has grown up around this, and there are two methods. One is to stick large gel pads on to the torso and the legs. These are attached to a machine that regulates temperature. When the body reaches the right temperature, it keeps it there for 24 hours. The other way is to put a catheter into the groin or neck, and cool the blood down as it passes by the catheter.

PROFILE
Sam Parnia is a director of resuscitation research at Stony Brook University Medical Center. His latest book is *The Lazarus Effect: The science that is erasing the boundaries between life and death* (Rider), sold as *Erasing Death* (HarperOne) in the US

Cooling benefits the heart and all the tissues, but we focus on the brain. There are also new methods in which people are cooled through the nose. You put tubes in the nostrils and inject cold vapour to cool the brain down selectively before the rest of the body.

If I had a cardiac arrest today, what are the chances I would get all of that?
Almost zero.

Why isn't this type of care routine?
Cardiac arrest is the only medical condition that will affect every single one of us eventually, unfortunately. What's frightening is that the way we are managed depends on where we are and who is involved. Even in the

Photography: Martin Adolfsson for *New Scientist*

same hospital, shift to shift, you will get a different level of care. There is no external regulation, so it's left to individuals.

There is disagreement over the interpretation of near death experiences (NDEs) - such as seeing a tunnel or a bright light. When a person dies, when do these experiences shut off?
One of the last things to fall into the realm of science has been the study of death. And now we have pushed back the boundary of death. In order to ensure that patients come back to life and don't have brain damage, we have to study the processes that go on after they die. Whether we like it or not, we have gone into the "afterlife" or whatever you want to call it.
For people who have NDEs, they are very

real. Most are convinced that what they saw is a glimpse of what it's like when we die. Most come back and have no fear of death, and are transformed in a positive way – becoming more altruistic. As a scientific community we have tried to explain these away, but we haven't been successful.

So how can a doctor, or any person of science, deal with such otherworldly experiences?
We have to accept that these experiences occur, that they are real to the people who

> ## "Consciousness is not annihilated when you reach the point of death"

have them, in the same way that if a patient has depression you would never say, "I know that you are feeling depressed but that is just an illusion. I'm the doctor. I'm going to tell you what your feelings really mean." But with NDEs, we do this all the time: "I know you think you saw this, but you really didn't."

Aren't NDEs just hallucinations?
We know from clinical tests that the brain doesn't function after death, therefore you can't even hallucinate. It's ridiculous to say that NDE people are hallucinating because you have to have a functioning brain. If I take a person in cardiac arrest and inject them with LSD, I guarantee you they will not hallucinate.

For your study of out of body experiences (OBEs), you placed images in hospital rooms on high shelves only someone floating near the ceiling could see. So far, two patients have had OBEs, but neither in a room with a shelf...
That's right. We had 25 hospitals that had an average of 500 beds working on the study. To put a shelf above every single bed, we would have to put up 12,500 shelves. That was completely unmanageable. We selected areas where cardiac arrest patients are frequently treated but even with that, at least half of those who had cardiac arrests and survived were in areas without shelves.

Are you continuing the experiment?
Yes. It's part of an overall package to improve resuscitation to the brain. We are trying not to forget during resuscitation that there's a human being in there.

In your book, you imply that death might be pleasant. Why do you think that?
The question is, what happens to human consciousness – the thing that makes me into who I am – when my heart stops beating and I die? From our external view, it looks like it simply disappears. But it sort of hibernates, in the same way as it does when you are given a general anaesthetic. And it comes back. I don't believe that your consciousness is annihilated when you reach the point of death. How far does it continue? I don't know. But I do know that at least in the period of time in which we can bring people back to life, that entity of the human mind has not been annihilated.

What does this mean?
Those people who have pleasant experiences after death suggest that we should not be afraid of the process. It means there is no reason to fear death. ▪

Out of thin air

Discovering how climbers and people who live at altitude cope with limited oxygen could bring big advances in medicine, finds **Ed Douglas**

SIXTY years after Edmund Hillary and Tenzing Norgay became the first people to climb Everest, the world's highest mountain is a busy place. When the weather is good in mid to late May, the upper slopes are crowded with hundreds of climbers. With every step available to view on YouTube, you might think there is nothing left to explore on the roof of the world. You would be wrong.

In 2013, a team from the Centre for Altitude, Space and Extreme Environment Medicine (CASE) at University College London made their second trip to Everest, and spent several weeks studying hundreds of trekkers, climbers and Sherpas. The findings from their work and that of others is radically changing our understanding of how our bodies adapt to altitude, particularly the low oxygen levels experienced there.

Don't assume this revolution only affects a few groups of people around the world. Anyone with anaemia, heart failure and a wide variety of other illnesses can experience low oxygen levels. In the UK, 1 in 5 people will end up in intensive care at some point in their lives, and a common feature of most of these patients is low oxygen – a state known as hypoxia. Doctors are stuck for ways to deal with the consequences (see also "Darwin's doctor", page 90). So could the adaptations of people who have evolved to live in these conditions point to new treatments?

Since 1953, a great deal of research has deepened our understanding of how humans adapt to life in the high mountains – and what can go wrong. The higher you go, the less oxygen the atmosphere contains. At La Rinconada in Peru, often cited as the highest town on Earth at 5100 metres above sea level, there is only around 50 per cent of the oxygen present at sea level. At the top of Everest, 8848 metres above sea level, it is just 33 per cent (see chart, page 102).

The body soon feels the effects. At first, moving around at altitude is immensely effortful – like wading through treacle while breathing through a straw. To compensate for low oxygen levels you breathe faster and deeper, a phenomenon called the hypoxic ventilatory response. Your heart rate and blood pressure increase, which can lead to life-threatening illnesses, notably high-altitude pulmonary and cerebral oedema, as fluid leaks from cells into cavities in your lungs and brain.

But you slowly adapt to the lack of oxygen: your body makes extra red blood cells and haemoglobin – the protein that carries oxygen through the bloodstream to the cells, where it is used in the production of energy. This ups the oxygen your cells receive, allowing your heart rate and blood pressure to fall, and you to breathe more easily and do athletic things like climbing mountains.

At least, that's the accepted wisdom. But CASE team member Hugh Montgomery, director of the UCL Institute for Human Health and Performance, has begun to question whether increasing haemoglobin is the most effective way to deal with hypoxia – or if it's just how your body responds. He points out that these are the same reactions that help us deal with blood loss. Perhaps, when the body senses low oxygen in the blood, it kicks off a chain of events that originally evolved to deal with injury. That would certainly make evolutionary sense. After all, injuries would have been a common danger for our forebears, whereas very few of our ancestors would have been climbing mountains.

There are many reasons why increasing haemoglobin isn't the best way to deal with hypoxia, says Montgomery, not least because it doesn't significantly improve the uptake of oxygen. That's because, at high altitude, less gas can dissolve into a liquid. This severely limits the amount of oxygen that can get into the blood, no matter how high its haemoglobin content. "Just increasing the red cell mass doesn't mean you're getting more oxygen to your cells," says Montgomery.

Increasing haemoglobin production also carries many risks. "It turns your blood to porridge," says Montgomery. "This is not good for you. It knackers your microcirculatory system." Thicker blood also leaves you more vulnerable to stroke, all of which adds up to a very poor adaptation to high altitude.

Evolved for the high life

This seems to suggest that increased haemoglobin is a side effect of hypoxia, rather than a solution, and more evidence comes from people living on the Tibetan plateau. In recent decades, the migration of Han Chinese on to the plateau has provided a natural experiment to study the adaptational differences between lowlanders and populations that have evolved over thousands of years to live at altitude.

In the 1990s, Lorna Moore and colleagues at the University of Colorado studied pregnancy and childbirth on the plateau, critical periods from an evolutionary perspective. They ❯

Insights gained at the top of Everest could one day save your life

IMAGE BROKER/REX FEATURES

Living on high

Oxygen levels drop dramatically with altitude, but that hasn't stopped some populations from reaching great heights – and living there for thousands of years

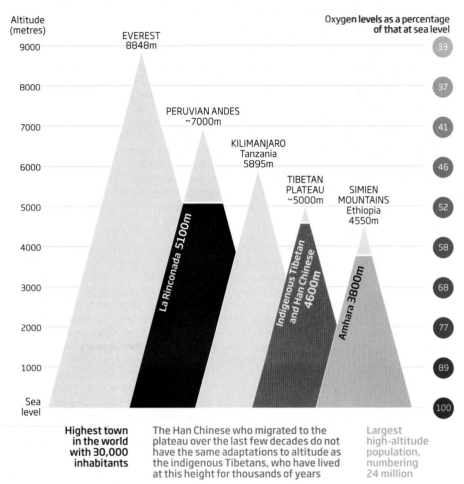

Altitude (metres)

Oxygen levels as a percentage of that at sea level

EVEREST 8848m — 33
— 37
PERUVIAN ANDES ~7000m — 41
KILIMANJARO Tanzania 5895m — 46
TIBETAN PLATEAU ~5000m / SIMIEN MOUNTAINS Ethiopia 4550m — 52
— 58
— 68
— 77
— 89
— 100

La Rinconada 5100m

Indigenous Tibetan and Han Chinese 4600m

Amhara 3800m

Highest town in the world with 30,000 inhabitants

The Han Chinese who migrated to the plateau over the last few decades do not have the same adaptations to altitude as the indigenous Tibetans, who have lived at this height for thousands of years

Largest high-altitude population, numbering 24 million

The people of La Rinconada, Peru, suffer many of the negative effects of altitude

found that, like Western tourists on Everest, Han women produce extra haemoglobin during pregnancy, making them vulnerable to the side effects of stickier blood, including stroke and thrombosis. Elevated blood pressure also brings a higher risk of eclampsia.

This is in stark contrast to the physiology of pregnant Tibetans, who do not have elevated levels of haemoglobin – their levels are similar to those of people living at sea level. As a result, Tibetan women have fewer stillbirths and premature babies than the Han Chinese at altitude. Their newborns also have higher birthweights.

Mysteriously, all Tibetans have a surprisingly low level of oxygen in their blood, yet still seem able to supply their bodies with enough juice to fuel a healthy life. So it would appear that in a population that faces hypoxia on a daily basis, evolution bypassed the risks of thick, soupy blood by finding another way to deal with the suffocating conditions. Such findings are reinforced by recent work suggesting direct selection on the genes that control haemoglobin in the Tibetans. Rasmus Nielsen at the University of California,

Berkeley, and researchers from the Chinese Academy of Sciences in Beijing compared the DNA of 50 Tibetans living in villages at 4300 and 4600 metres high with 40 Han Chinese living in Beijing at just 43 metres above sea level. The biggest difference was in DNA near a gene called *EPAS1*, which regulates haemoglobin production. This was altered in 87 per cent of the Tibetans but only 9 per cent of the Chinese. Further studies have also found differences in *EGLN1*, which codes for a protein important in regulating the body's oxygen levels, and *PPARA*, which also seems to regulate haemoglobin production.

Converging paths

Genetic adaptations to lower oxygen can also be found in another high-altitude population: the Amhara, who have lived for around 70,000 years in Ethiopia's Simien mountains at altitudes of up to 3800 metres. Intriguingly, Cynthia Beall at Case Western Reserve University in Cleveland, Ohio, has found that, like the Tibetans, the Amhara have normal haemoglobin levels but involving mutations

on different genes. "All indications are we're seeing convergent evolution," she says. "On one level – the biological response – they are the same. On another level – the changes in the gene pool – they are different."

That two populations independently evolved different ways to limit haemoglobin production in response to low oxygen levels certainly lends weight to the idea that the textbook descriptions of hypoxia needs a rethink. Nevertheless, it's important to note that not all high-altitude populations have evolved the changes seen in the Tibetans and Amhara. People in the Andes, for instance, have high haemoglobin just like the Han Chinese and Western climbers. Tellingly, however, they are also more likely than Tibetans to suffer from problems such as high blood pressure, palpitations and fatigue.

More work is needed to understand exactly how all these populations cope with low oxygen, and how such knowledge might be used in a medical setting. Many illnesses affecting the respiratory and cardiovascular systems result in reduced oxygen supply to the body's organs, leading to hypoxia. At the moment, it is very difficult to find out how the body reacts to this process in the hospital ward, or how to respond to increase the chances of survival. As Montgomery points out, "to tease out the pathways, you have to take people and make them hypoxic for long enough to work out how they are adapting" – hardly an ethical experiment to try in the lab or on patients.

In the past, most efforts in intensive care have centred on improving the supply of oxygen. But the fact that Tibetans can live with permanently low levels of blood oxygen, without any ill effects, might suggest other ways to deal with the problem.

One possible answer stems from the discovery that Tibetans have unusually high levels of nitric oxide in their blood. This dilates

JOHNNY HAGLUND/GETTY

A FISHY SOLUTION

The history of adaptation to hypoxia is a lot older than our species. Since oxygen appeared in the atmosphere 2.45 billion years ago, there have been several anoxic events, especially in the oceans. Life had to find ways of dealing with lowered oxygen – and some of the species are still alive today.

When the thermometer drops and their ponds freeze over, crucian carp (*Carassius carassius*) survive the anoxic conditions partly by slowing their metabolism but mostly using a clever metabolic trick: anaerobic respiration. The fish turn reserves of glycogen built up over summer into glucose and ethanol, releasing energy in the process. Crucian carp have been shown to survive anoxic conditions for up to 140 days using this method.

Crucian carp brains have a large store of glycogen, which has alarmed dissectionists unprepared for the fish's ability to survive being disconnected from its heart for several hours.

Producing ethanol as a by-product of hypoxia might appeal to some climbers. The UK barrister and mountaineer Terry Mooney once observed that since climbing at altitude was like going to work with a hangover, then the best training for Everest should involve spending as much time in the pub as possible.

vessels, allowing larger volumes of blood to move through the body in the same amount of time. Together with their deeper and faster breathing patterns, this could explain how Tibetans move enough oxygen to their tissues. If so, CASE researchers hope they can use their understanding of this process to improve the delivery of oxygen in hospital patients.

Another idea being explored by the CASE team is that the secret to coping with altitude lies in using the limited oxygen more efficiently, through an altered metabolism. On the CASE team's first Everest expedition in 2007, Denny Levett took muscle samples from 17 climbers at base camp and sent them to Andrew Murray at the University of Cambridge. The samples revealed that during the early days at base camp, muscle cells mothballed some of their mitochondria, presumably so that if conditions became less hypoxic they could get them working again. However, after several weeks, cells had lost 20 per cent of their mitochondria. "This striking finding might suggest that when oxygen supply is limited, the muscle chooses to sacrifice some of its energy-requiring functions in favour of maintaining others," says Murray.

These changes may form part of the process of acclimatisation experienced by trekkers and climbers going to altitude. But do they also reflect what happens in people who have evolved to cope with low oxygen? Murray's team has now conducted similar experiments to compare lowlanders' muscles with those of Sherpas before and after acclimatisation. The results are not yet finalised, but he predicts that Sherpas have evolved protection against a drop in cell function, which could explain their superior performance at altitude.

Might it be possible to induce similar metabolic changes in hospital patients? "The therapeutic direction this is taking us in is to try to help the body reduce oxygen consumption, rather than driving delivery as was previously the case," says Montgomery.

Understanding this mechanism will also shed light on the factors that limit a patient's long-term recovery. Both lowlanders trekking up Everest and hospital patients often show rapid weight loss following hypoxia. A loss of appetite makes sense if your metabolism slows down to reduce oxygen consumption, but these changes can take a long time to reverse once conditions have returned to normal, supporting the idea that hypoxia turns the body into a lean-burn engine. "Eighty per cent of people of working age can't go back to work a year after leaving an intensive care unit. They've got nothing left," says Montgomery.

Weight loss is a particular problem for people with respiratory illnesses like chronic obstructive pulmonary disease. Since Sherpas don't seem to pay the same metabolic price as lowlanders in the face of hypoxia, understanding these differences may help us manage these symptoms, says Murray.

These are potentially the first of many lines of enquiry, as the CASE team work through the data from their latest trip. What's clear is that we are only just beginning to understand the human body's ability to evolve and adapt to extreme existence. That is why, 60 years after it was first climbed, the high drama of our struggle on Everest continues to offer new horizons. ■

"The migration of Han Chinese to the Tibetan plateau offers a natural experiment to compare lowlanders and populations evolved for life at high altitude"

Tibetan children remain energetic when most Westerners would be gasping for breath

KIERAN DODDS/PANOS

Erase your fear...

... or banish your addictions with the help of memory-boosting pills. **Jessica Hamzelou** faces her own phobia to find out more

IT'S happening again. My heart starts pounding and my pulse races. I can feel my face flush and my palms start to sweat. It is all I can do to prevent myself from breaking into a full-blown panic attack. And yet I'm not in any real danger. I'm just at the top of an escalator, making my way down to a London Underground rail platform, along with hundreds of other Londoners who don't seem fazed in the slightest – but the sight of the drop below me is the stuff of my nightmares.

This scenario will sound familiar to the many other people with phobias. All it takes is a worrying thought or glimpse – whether of a steep drop or a spider's web – for the mind and body to race into panicked overdrive. These fears are difficult to conquer, largely because the best way of getting over a phobia is to expose yourself to your fear many times over.

But there may be a shortcut. Drugs that work to boost learning may help someone with a phobia to "detrain their brain", losing the fearful associations that fuel their panic. This approach is also showing promise for a host of other problems – from chemical and gambling addictions to obsessive nail-biting. In a bid to find out if it really works, I head to West Virginia to take part in a trial.

The brain's extraordinary ability to pick up new memories and forge associations is so well celebrated that its dark side is often neglected. In the case of a phobia, it may have been an unpleasant experience that once triggered a panicked response to spiders, mice or, for me, heights, leading the feelings to resurface whenever we see the relevant cue. Former drug addicts have similarly learned responses when they see something that reminds them of their habit: the sight of rolled-up banknotes for a cocaine user, for instance.

So how do we overcome such deep-seated associations? One answer is exposure therapy, a treatment primarily used to deal with anxiety and phobias. In those initial studies, people gradually expose themselves to increasingly anxiety-triggering situations – called a "fear hierarchy" – until they feel at ease with them. In my case, that would involve scaling a series of ever greater heights.

As the individual becomes more comfortable with each situation, they create a new memory – one that links the cue with reduced feelings of anxiety, rather than the sensations marking the onset of a panic attack.

This process is called extinction learning.

Unfortunately, while it is relatively easy to create a fear-based memory, expunging that fear is pretty hard work. Each of those exposure trials will probably involve a great deal of stress and anxiety, leading some psychotherapists to conclude that the treatment is unethical.

For that reason, neuroscientists have been looking for new ways to speed up extinction learning. One such avenue is the use of "cognitive enhancers", and one of the most promising contenders is an antibiotic originally used to treat tuberculosis. Apart from its action on germs, D-cycloserine, or DCS, also acts on neurons. The drug slots into part of the NMDA receptor – a site that seems to modulate neurons' ability to adjust their signalling in response to events. This tuning of a neuron's firing is thought to be one of the key ways the brain stores memories, and at very low doses, DCS appears to boost that process, improving our ability to learn.

In 2004, Kerry Ressler at Emory University in Atlanta, Georgia, and his colleagues were among the first to test whether DCS could also help people with phobias. They performed a pilot trial on 28 people undergoing exposure therapy for acrophobia – a fear of heights. Sure enough, they found that those given a small amount of DCS alongside their therapy were able to reduce their phobia to a greater extent than those given a placebo. Since then, other groups have replicated the finding in many more trials.

Future research may show ways to refine the method further. It still takes a long time to accomplish even one of the steps on a person's fear hierarchy, says Cristian Sirbu, a behavioural scientist and psychologist at ▶

Tall tales: is a pill to banish phobias too good to be true?

West Virginia University in Charleston. "You end up with a patient feeling that they failed," he says. Instead, he thinks that DCS may make it possible to tackle the problem in a single 3-hour session, which is long enough to make real headway and end with a feeling of satisfaction. To find out if Sirbu's approach could work for me and others like me, and if a dose of DCS could boost the effects, I landed in Charleston to take part in a trial.

It started with a battery of tests. To get a good handle on my phobia, Sirbu and his colleague interviewed me before giving me some physical tests. First, the pair hooked me up to electrodes to measure my heart rate and fingertip sweatiness, before sitting me in front of a video of a pair of gardeners walking around a rose garden, discussing its merits. The team were trying to get an idea of how my body functioned in a relaxed state, before we moved on to actual heights.

With the electrodes still attached, I was asked to approach a second-storey balcony. The team recorded increases in heart rate and sweating as I started to panic – business as usual for me.

The exciting part of the study kicks off a week later, when I am given a tablet to swallow – I don't know whether it is DCS or merely a sugar pill – before starting my 3-hour therapy session. The therapy itself is a gruelling experience to say the least. After walking down a windowed corridor on the fifth floor of a building, Sirbu and I head to the hospital's stairwell. With a huge visible drop to one side of me, it is terrifying. Our voices echo and I try to focus on the dust bunnies lying on each step. But after an exhausting 3 hours I start to have a full-blown panic attack which prevents me from reaching Sirbu's goal of climbing two floors up the staircase.

Rewrite or delete

What went wrong? Phobias come in different flavours, and more intense fears can take more work to overcome. Because I needed another session, Sirbu pulled me out of the clinical trial. He then tells me that I had taken the active drug, not the placebo. It is a disappointing result, particularly after hearing about Sirbu's promising results with other trial participants, all of whom experienced some kind of benefit from the session, he tells me.

Ultimately, trying to erase a fear response in a single trial may just be too ambitious for someone with a phobia as extreme as mine. What is more, Merel Kindt, who studies anxiety disorders at the University of

DAVID SEYMOUR/MAGNUM

Can we return to the fearless bliss of childhood?

Amsterdam in the Netherlands, is sceptical that its benefits would last. She points out that although Sirbu's approach attempts to lay down calmer associations, it doesn't directly undo the fearful response that is also embedded in our memories, so there's always a chance of relapse. Indeed, since the therapy had failed while I took the cognitive enhancer, I am concerned that I may have instead laid down even more stressful memories – a potential problem with the method that has troubled some researchers.

But there may be another way. Rather than simply trying to overlay the fearful associations with a new one, Kindt is instead trying to alter them at their source. To do so, her method targets an entirely different pathway from the trials using DCS. It is based on the idea that every time we access a memory, be it of a specific recollection or a learned reaction, we temporarily put it in a fragile state. Normally, the updated memory is then reconsolidated by the formation of new proteins that make the necessary synaptic changes. If stress hormones like adrenaline are washing around the body – as is often the case during the fearful reactions of someone gripped by a phobia – the original memory's emotional force is maintained. But a beta-blocker drug called propranolol

can block the adrenaline from binding to the neurons, which Kindt hopes will interfere with the process to stop the emotional trauma associated with the cue from being reinforced. "We don't erase the memory, but we can erase the learned fear response," she says. A similar approach is being investigated to soothe the fearful flashbacks that haunt people with post-traumatic stress disorder.

Kindt's team is currently testing its effectiveness with arachnophobia – by giving people propranolol while they look at spiders, for example. "It's very successful," she says. "The participants said they still didn't like spiders, but they were able to approach a tarantula." Kindt, who is preparing the findings for publication, says the benefit was still there when she checked three months later.

As the work to treat phobias gains momentum, others are looking at whether the same strategies could work with addictions. After all, phobias and addictions share some similarities. "They are both habitual, emotional, reflexive responses," says Ressler.

Here, the idea is to expose a person to a "trigger environment" associated with taking a drug. That might be the sight of a cigarette for instance. But in therapy sessions, the individual isn't allowed their substance of choice, helping them learn how to resist the urge (see also "The

"Arachnophobes were able to approach tarantulas after the treatment"

virtual therapist will see you now", page 122).

Elizabeth Santa Ana, now at the Medical University of South Carolina in Charleston, has tested whether DCS could boost this method, using a group of smokers. "People would sit in a room with a packet of their favourite cigarettes, take a cigarette and hold it up to their mouth, but not smoke it," she says. At the same time, Santa Ana taught them coping skills, and encouraged them with guided imagery. "For example, I would ask them to imagine having tar all over their bodies, and then imagine being able to breathe freely once they'd stopped smoking," she says.

Forgotten cravings

In the group of 25 participants, 13 were given a small dose of DCS during their time in the lab, while the rest took a placebo. For the preliminary study, the team did not ask the participants to give up smoking. Instead, they measured the smokers' cravings a week after the therapy – by asking them how great an urge to smoke they felt, and measuring how much they sweated when faced with a cigarette they were not supposed to light.

The team found that people who had been given a dose of DCS exhibited a reduced sweating response to smoking cues, and also reported a lower desire to smoke. "There were both objective and subjective differences between the two groups," says Santa Ana. "They were promising findings."

Clearly, it will take more trials to find out if the approach actually helps people quit smoking for good. In any case, it looks likely that other strategies would be needed to extinguish cravings for other drugs; trials of

cocaine-addicted people using DCS did not report reduced desire for a hit, for instance.

Propranolol – the beta blocker that Kindt was using to "destabilise" the learned responses of people with arachnophobia – may be more fruitful. In a study in 2013, 50 people addicted to cocaine watched videos of people taking the drug. Half of the group had been given a small dose of propranolol immediately after watching the films. A day later, they were asked to watch the films again, but they reported that the intensity of their cravings had fallen significantly more than the control group. The participants also showed a reduced physiological response to the cues. With more sessions, it may therefore be possible to cut the long-term risk of relapse.

One of the reasons that addictive cravings are particularly difficult to target is that the addictions themselves can make long-lasting changes to brain chemistry. When people hooked on drugs like cocaine attempt to withdraw from the substance, they experience a drop in brain levels of glutamate – a neurotransmitter that acts to fire up neurons. This imbalance damages communication between the decision-making prefrontal cortex and the nucleus accumbens – the region involved in pleasure-seeking and reward-learning, potentially explaining why people with addictions find it so difficult to develop the neural pathways necessary to reverse their habits and control their cravings.

For this reason, some teams have turned to supplements like n-acetyl cysteine (NAC), which seems to help return levels of glutamate to normal. NAC has shown promise in studies that reversed the drug-seeking behaviours of rats addicted to cocaine and heroin. In

Spiders improve on acquaintance

addition, a series of small trials showed that NAC reduces craving in people who are still using cocaine. People who were considered to have a problematic dependency on cannabis, meanwhile, were more than twice as likely to show no signs of drug use in a urine test after taking NAC for eight weeks, compared with those taking a placebo. The treatment has also shown positive results for gambling addicts and chronic nail-biters. It is important to note that the NAC treatments did not involve explicit forms of exposure therapy; rather, the participants were learning to cope with their cravings as they went about their daily lives. So it would be interesting to know what the results with NAC would be like if combined with sessions with a therapist that directly aimed to extinguish the responses to drug cues. Some research groups are interested in testing the possibility.

It is still early days. The disappointing results of my trial are enough to convince me that these would-be treatments for phobias and addiction aren't miracle cures. For most people, changing unwanted habits or reactions will involve dedication and perseverance. And since much of the research into drugs such as DCS has been primarily pilot studies, it will be important to see if similar results show up in bigger clinical trials. But if just one of these possible treatments comes up trumps, it could change many blighted lives.

As it is, I'm going to have to trust that good things come to those who wait. Although the "flash therapy" for my phobia did not work for me, I'm now trying a more drawn-out version of exposure therapy. It's hard going, but right now I'm four steps through my 10-step programme and happy to say that I'm already reaching new heights. ▪

Old habits die hard – unless you get a memory boost

RIGHT: PATRICK MOURRAL/PICTURETANK; FAR RIGHT: ROBERTO BOCCIARDO/AURORA

FOR Goran Ostovich*, just driving his delivery van was a daily agony. The painful swelling in his hands, wrists and elbows made it nearly impossible to grip and turn the wheel – never mind loading and unloading the produce his van carried. The drugs that he had taken for years to alleviate his rheumatoid arthritis didn't help much. He had reluctantly abandoned his favourite sport, ping-pong. He stopped working. The final cruelty was when he could no longer lift his young children or play with them.

It was then that Ostovich volunteered for a last resort treatment: he had a small computer implanted in his neck that would instruct his immune cells to stand down.

Ostovich's implant is a harbinger of a revolution in the pharmaceutical industry. Researchers are waking up to the idea that the electrical language of nerves might be spoken more widely in the body than anyone thought, playing a pivotal role in coordinating the actions of our organs, glands and cells. It may

pathways throughout the body. For example, to regulate your heartbeat, sensory nerve fibres detect your heart rate and relay that information to the brain, which in turn sends instructions back to the heart telling it to speed up or slow down. A similar circuit controls blood pressure. "It's like setting a thermostat," says Kevin Tracey of the Feinstein Institute for Medical Research in New York. "The nervous system constantly responds to changes and adjusts everything back to the set point." We can manipulate that electrical language when the body's natural thermostat goes wrong, with defibrillators that use electricity to jump-start a stalled heart, or pacemakers that regulate the rate at which it pumps blood.

No such central governor was thought to control the immune system. A decentralised army, including white blood cells and virus-eating macrophages, was thought to roam around in the bloodstream fighting ad hoc battles against bacteria and viruses where

The vital spark

Electricity's role in the body has long been overlooked. Now, finds **Linda Geddes**, we are finally beginning to harness its power

even be possible to use the nervous system to coax the body into healing itself in ways we never dreamed of.

The pharmaceutical industry is on the case, and a spate of projects is under way around the world to map the exact circuits that allow the nervous system to intervene when things go wrong in the body. Autoimmune diseases, asthma, diabetes and gastric conditions are just a few of the disorders that appear amenable to electrical intervention. There are even hints it could be used as a radical way of treating cancer. Within a decade or two, electrical implants could replace many common drugs. Welcome to the brave new world of electroceuticals.

The idea that electrical signals can control the immune system will sound bizarre to anyone who has studied biology. After all, electricity is the language of the nervous system, not the immune system. Electrical signals, in the form of action potentials, travel to and from the brain via the numerous nerve

they needed to be fought. Damaged tissue might send out a call for reinforcements, but there was no central command.

Tracey challenged that understanding in the late 1990s. He and his colleagues were testing a new anti-inflammatory drug. When they injected it into rats' brains, they noticed it also dampened inflammation in their limbs and peripheral organs. "The amount of drug we were using was vanishingly small so we knew the signal wasn't going through the bloodstream," Tracey says. The only explanation was the nervous system. The idea was too intriguing to ignore. "So we started stimulating different nerves to see if we could reproduce the effect," he says. Sure enough, he found that electrically stimulating the nerve fibres that linked to the spleen – home to immune cells known as T-cells – dampened their activity. It was one of the first hints that the brain might be talking to the immune system after all.

But how? Tracey had discovered that ❯

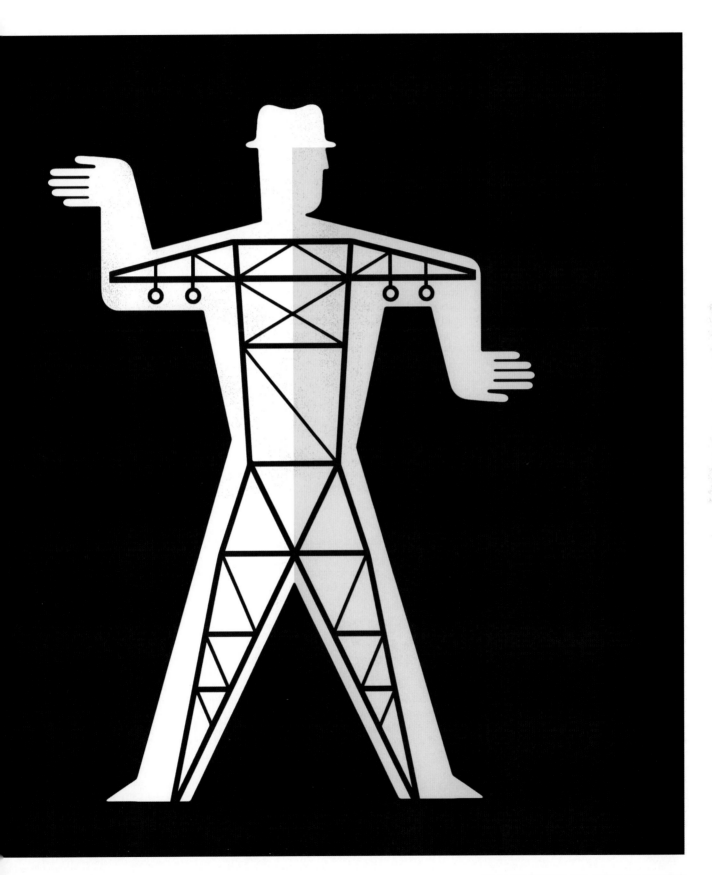

nerve cells speak to immune cells in the spleen using chemicals called neurotransmitters – the same language they use to speak to each other. Nerve stimulation triggered a complex reaction that told the T-cells to stop the production of inflammatory substances, such as tumour necrosis factor (TNF).

In healthy people this nerve circuit ensures that levels of TNF never get too high. However, in autoimmune disorders such as rheumatoid arthritis, the normal brakes fail and TNF production spirals out of control. It accumulates in people's joints, triggering pain, inflammation and the breakdown of tissue.

To stave off these debilitating effects, people with rheumatoid arthritis often turn to drugs called TNF inhibitors. However, because these mop up all the TNF they find, they leave people at increased risk of infection. Worse, they don't always work for rheumatoid arthritis. Ostovich was on several different drugs, but his pain was still debilitating.

But he was fortunate. The clinic he attended had just started recruiting people for a trial of a therapy based on Tracey's findings. Following successful animal studies, Tracey had founded a company called SetPoint Medical to treat arthritis in people. For its pilot trial, SetPoint chose Ostovich's home country, Bosnia and Herzegovina, where few have access to TNF inhibitors. The plan was to implant tiny computers into the necks of 12 people with rheumatoid arthritis to see if electrical stimulation eased their symptoms.

Ostovich's computer tapped into his vagus nerve, the electrical superhighway that links the brain to all of the major organs, to intermittently stimulate the nerve fibres that connect to the spleen (see diagram, below). The researchers hoped that the device would instruct his immune system to stand down and stop attacking his joints.

It worked. The constant pain in Ostovich's joints stopped. Levels of an inflammatory protein called CRP that is usually elevated in people with arthritis fell back to normal. Best of all, this intervention had no serious side effects. Nerve stimulation only removes around 80 per cent of TNF – as opposed to eliminating it the way drugs do. It also suppresses the production of other immune factors that can damage tissue when released in excess. Like Ostovich, seven other volunteers showed similar improvements.

With this triumph, Tracey believes that he has identified the first of many neural circuits that control the immune system. In 2013, Clifford Woolf of Harvard Medical School announced that he and his colleagues had found a second: nerves in the skin, which were able to suppress infection when stimulated. Similar circuits are cropping up elsewhere too. The carotid body – a cluster of cells that sense glucose levels in the main artery carrying blood to the head – has a connection to the central nervous system that can affect rats'

insulin sensitivity and blood pressure. Implanted electrodes, says Silvia Conde at the New University of Lisbon in Portugal, where the study was conducted, might manipulate some nerve signals and not others, making it possible to tweak insulin sensitivity without disrupting other vital functions of the carotid body. At any rate, it is becoming clear that these circuits are all plugged into a body-wide electrical grid.

The voltage cure

But as Conde's work implies, the immune system isn't the only thing these circuits can manipulate. Electrocore, an electroceutical device manufacturer with headquarters in Basking Ridge, New Jersey, has been working to isolate a different set of fibres within the vagus nerve to treat asthma. "A nerve is like a transatlantic telephone wire," Tracey says. "It has lots of individual cables inside it." The nerve fibres targeted by Electrocore's neck stimulator link to a region of the brain involved in the physiological response to stress and panic. Zapping them triggers the release of noradrenaline, which dampens the activity of neurons that control the airways, prompting them to open, averting the asthma attack. "The message we're sending is: 'everything's fine, you can relax, there's no fight or flight to engage in'," says Electrocore CEO J. P. Errico.

It appears to work. In 81 people admitted to emergency departments during an asthma attack who didn't respond to standard drugs within an hour, electrical stimulation with Electrocore's implanted electrode led to a significant improvement in their lung function. The company is now investigating whether its implant might help lessen symptoms in people with other conditions as well as asthma, including irritable bowel syndrome and migraine.

Although vagus nerve stimulation is an attractive strategy, it may not be focused enough, says Brendan Canning of the Johns Hopkins Asthma and Allergy Center in Baltimore, Maryland. The nerve fibres Electrocore targets are unlikely to combat some of the other troublesome symptoms of asthma, such as coughing and the feeling that you are not getting enough air, he says. Canning has discovered that these symptoms are controlled by a different set of fibres in the vagus nerve. However, stimulating these also triggers "fight or flight" responses such as boosting the heart and breathing rate, which often exacerbate an attack by

A shock to the system

One way to stop the immune system from attacking itself is to implant an electrical stimulator in the neck, which intermittently stimulates the vagus nerve

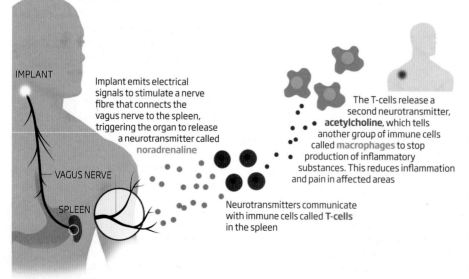

IMPLANT

Implant emits electrical signals to stimulate a nerve fibre that connects the vagus nerve to the spleen, triggering the organ to release a neurotransmitter called noradrenaline

VAGUS NERVE

SPLEEN

The T-cells release a second neurotransmitter, acetylcholine, which tells another group of immune cells called macrophages to stop production of inflammatory substances. This reduces inflammation and pain in affected areas

Neurotransmitters communicate with immune cells called T-cells in the spleen

activating a person's panic response.

Such early measures are relatively blunt instruments. No existing implant is able to isolate individual cables. Instead, SetPoint's implants use a workaround: they are tuned so that the amount of electricity you put in only stimulates a small subset of the cables.

It's an elegant fix, but what if you could also eavesdrop on the electrical signals to detect abnormalities and only speak to the fibres that were misfiring? Such a smart electrode, Canning says, could also "detect changes in nerve activity, provide therapy as needed and then shut off".

This is exactly what global pharmaceutical giant GlaxoSmithKline (GSK) is working on. "The goal is to have rice-sized implants that sit on the peripheral nerves and record the complexity of the electrical language that flows through them, detect when something's out of balance and then fix it," says Kristoffer Famm of GSK. "We believe this treatment could be crucial for a whole host of chronic diseases – things like diabetes, hypertension, arthritis and chronic pain."

Tracey and Woolf's research shows that achieving Famm's goal is possible, although commercialising it will be more difficult. It will require collaboration between scientists who don't usually interact – engineers that design brain-machine interfaces, say, and lung or immunology experts. In December 2013, GSK hosted a forum in New York to identify the key hurdles most likely to stop the field of electroceuticals from progressing, and offered a $1 million bounty to the group that overcomes them.

That reward is only a fraction of what the firm is spending on electroceuticals. GSK has funded six centres to begin teasing apart the neural circuits that underlie specific diseases. Unofficially, 11 more have joined the team.

And while GSK may have the biggest budget, it is by no means the only company betting big

"By manipulating electrical signals in cells, they regrew the frog's amputated leg"

on this technology. Beyond Electrocore, the field includes medical device giant Medtronic, which is working on electrical interference for stubborn gastrointestinal problems. "We're learning to speak the electrical language of the body," says Famm. GSK expects to treat a range of common disorders with electrical implants.

Yet even that may be just the tip of the iceberg. Electroceuticals may also offer new avenues to treat cancer.

The reason nerve cells can transmit electrical signals is because the inside of the cell is negatively charged relative to the outside, known as its resting potential. When a nerve cell fires, there is a sudden influx of positive ions into the cell through channels in its membrane. These ion channels open and close much more quickly in nerve cells, but other cells speak this electrical language too. "All cells maintain a resting potential. They use it signal to their neighbours," says Michael Levin of Tufts University in Medford, Massachusetts.

Each kind of cell has its own resting potential, and Levin has discovered that these differences play a key role in determining which embryonic cells turn into what part of the body during development. In frog embryos, for example, setting the voltage of what are normally destined to become gut cells to the normal range of eye cells triggered the growth of complete eyes in the embryo's gut. "A lot of this can be done using drugs that are already in human use," he says.

Levin has taken it even further. By soaking the stump of a frog's amputated leg in a cocktail of drugs that trigger the flow of sodium ions into cells, his lab has managed to coax adult frogs to grow new legs – something which is not normally possible.

Intrigued, he wondered whether he could reverse this logic to inhibit unwanted cells. In 2013, he successfully used ion channel drugs to stop the growth of tumours in tadpoles primed to develop cancer.

Levin's work is early, and electroceuticals won't cure every disease – but we should expect to see a lot more stories like Ostovich's. Eight weeks after getting his implant, he returned to work. When Tracey heard the success story, he says, "I said, 'I have to meet this guy'".

Tracey speaks no Bosnian and Ostovich speaks no English, so the meeting required a translator. But conversation was hardly necessary to see that the treatment had changed Ostovich's life. "The expression on his face was unbridled joy, gratitude and relief," Tracey says. "It made all the years of basic bench research worthwhile." Ostovich told Tracey that the device had worked so well he had been able to take up ping pong again. And he felt so great after playing ping pong that he decided to try tennis. Indeed, this may have revealed a potential downside of the device: in his pain-free enthusiasm, he overdid it and ended up with a tennis-related knee injury. His doctors were forced to caution the man who, just two months earlier was unable to play with his children, to take it easy. ∎

Name has been changed to protect confidentiality

The memory fix

Implants that bridge damaged parts of the brain are no longer a distant dream, says **Sally Adee**

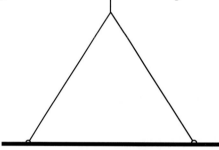

SAM DEADWYLER's work sounded a little too much like something from *The Matrix* – and that was a big problem. In the same way that Neo downloads a kung fu master's skills, Deadwyler had wired up the brain of a rat with electronics that transplanted memories derived from 30 rats into its brain, allowing it to draw on training that it had never personally experienced. The study had the potential to be a landmark finding – but "everyone thought it was science fiction", he says. "I thought, 'no one's going to believe this unless I do a hundred control experiments'."

So he did just that. In 2013 – 10 years after the original experiment – the paper was published at last. Instant kung fu is still the stuff of Hollywood blockbusters, but this research could nevertheless have a huge impact on many people living with brain damage. Ultimately, the same kind of neural implants that allowed memories to be "donated" from many rats into another individual could restore lost brain function after an accident, a stroke or Alzheimer's disease.

For a lot of people with memory loss, damaged parts of the brain are failing to pass information from one area to another. If you could create electronics that interpret the signals from one area, circumvent the damaged parts, and write them into the second area, you could help people regain the ability to form new memories, or even gain access to precious old ones. Such a chip would act as a kind of brain bypass.

Getting there won't be easy: an implant of this kind requires neuroscience that is only now beginning to be understood. More than that, though, these technologies raise entirely new ethical questions. Our memories define us, so preserving them from damage could save our identity – but when your memory is a computer algorithm, are you still the same person? It's almost time to find out: the first human studies could be under way by 2020.

Our ability to communicate directly with the brain has accelerated rapidly over the past two decades. The technology – known as brain-machine interfaces – has restored hearing and sight in the form of cochlear and retinal implants. It has also helped people control prosthetic limbs: some robotic arms, connected to the motor cortex, now have such sensitivity that amputees can hold a cup of coffee, pick individual grapes and even play the guitar.

Impressive as they are, however, these devices have a limited job. "The prosthetic limbs are mainly about output – we read one area of the brain and use it to control a device," says Robert Hampson, who works on cognitive implants with Deadwyler at Wake Forest Baptist Medical Center in North Carolina. "And the retinal and cochlear implants are input devices. We take output from a machine and input it to one part of the brain."

When translating between two areas of the brain, however, you need a device that can do both: record activity from one set of neurons and then electrically stimulate another set of neurons to replay it whenever it is needed. Needless to say, it's an endeavour rife with challenges. "To make a cognitive device, we first have to know what a memory looks like," says Hampson. The search for a memory trace in the brain has been complicated by the fact that there are many different kinds of memories: there's the short-term "working memory" that helps you to remember a phone number before you dial, sense memories that might include the echo of what someone's just said, and long-term memories of facts, skills and experiences. It is this long-term recall, and how it emerges from working memory, that Deadwyler and Hampson are interested in.

Although each memory trace is different, all long-term memories begin life in a region called the hippocampus, the brain's "printing press". Place an implant here and it might be possible to record memories as they form. The next step is to figure out the neural code that represents a particular memory. The key is thought to lie in the exact firing pattern of ▶

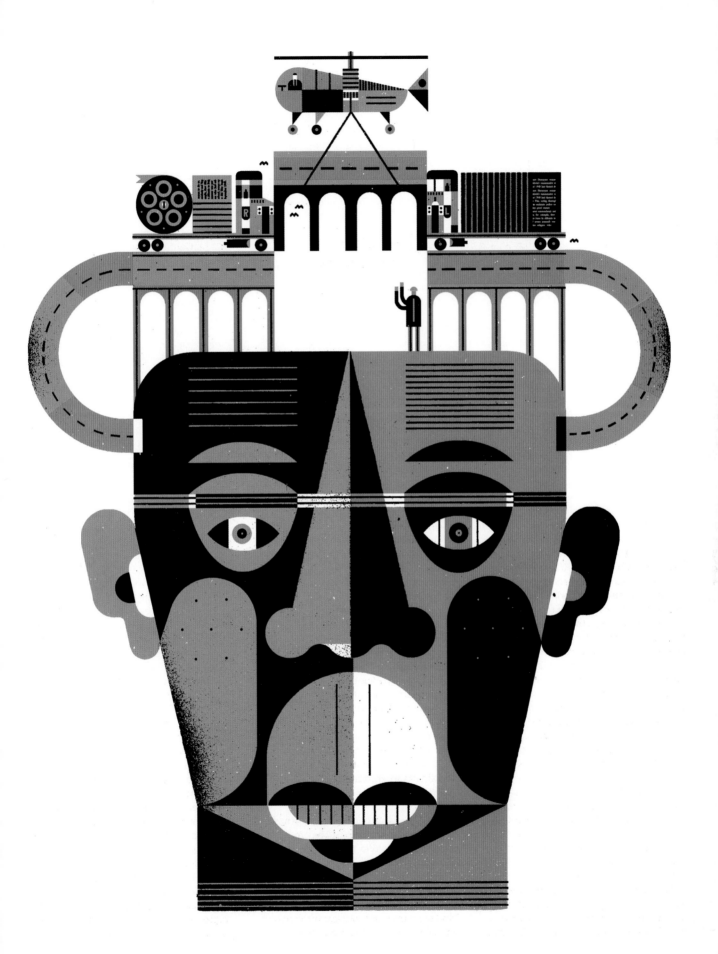

SOURCE CODE

We've come a long way in our ability to decode the meaning of the brain's signals – far enough to allow people to control wheelchairs with their thoughts and perhaps even restore their ability to form new memories (see main feature).

But before you can tease out what the brain's signals might mean, you first need a high-fidelity signal. There are many ways to eavesdrop on the brain's electrical communications, and they're all about trade-offs. Think of it as a night at a concert. Non-invasive electrodes on the scalp can listen to the entire orchestra. You can zero in on the string section by getting a little more invasive with electrocorticography, which involves placing a sheet of electrodes on the surface of the brain. But if you want to listen to an individual violin, you have no choice but make direct contact with individual neurons.

Such precision requires inserting deep-penetrating electrodes – which come with several drawbacks. Their insertion can rip and slice the surrounding neurons, causing oedema and scarring, and the brain's immune response forms scars that wall off the invading object. Soon, the electrodes can no longer read any meaningful information.

As a result, few implants have lasted more than a year or two. "Ideally you want a lifetime implant," says Mohammad Reza Abidian of Pennsylvania State University in University Park. We may soon be able to extend their life expectancy by "up to 10 years". Abidian has surveyed what neuroscientists are exploring for the next generation of electrodes.

1. Shrink
Creating thinner wires mitigates one of the major mechanical issues with brain implants – the fundamental mismatch between a hard, rigid electrode and a soft, squishy brain. The thinner you make them – and some are now nanofilaments – the more bendy they become and the less they'll irritate the brain.

2. Camouflage
No matter how thin, penetrating electrodes will give themselves away as foreign objects because they are made of silicon with metal tips. Some scientists are looking into biocompatible materials and hydrogels to render the interlopers invisible. Wrapping polymer electrodes in silk is another option, allowing them to easily slide into soft brain tissue. Once inside, the silk dissolves and is absorbed by the brain – without an immune response. But even biocompatible materials won't fool the brain's immune cells all the time.

3. Infiltrate
To really blend in, you need to trick the brain into thinking your implant is alive. To do this, some researchers are looking into organic electrodes, made of materials such as polymers and hydrogels, which are most famously found in contact lenses.

4. Seduce
A perfect implant would not just be tolerated but also entice neurons into embracing the electrodes, growing into and around them. Neuronal connections tend to be insulated with myelin, so researchers at the University of California, San Francisco, have built polymer scaffolds that encourage brain cells to lay myelin around implants, which should improve the chances of making a good connection. Others are doping electrodes with neurotransmitters, proteins and nerve growth factors.

Besides listening to neurons, electrodes often need to stimulate them, which can also cause damage if done repeatedly. A left-field technique may minimise the intrusion.

Using a technique called optogenetics, researchers can use pulses of light to switch the genes inside individual neurons on or off. This should make it possible to pinpoint specific parts of the brain, the way only penetrating electrodes can now. There are even indications that it can be done without the fibre-optic cable that is currently necessary to deliver the light into the brain: passing certain wavelengths of light through an intact skull has shown promise.

There's just one catch. To make the cells sensitive to light, you need to insert a gene using gene therapy. Even so, neuroscientist Sam Deadwyler at Wake Forest University in North Carolina thinks that while using optogenetics in humans is a long way off, it's the only way cognitive prostheses will ever be used beyond people with brain injuries and diseases. "It's a technology that doesn't require you to put electrodes in the head," he says. "That would make it possible to adapt for general use."

In other words, if it doesn't require brain surgery, it's something people might use some day simply to improve their memory.

interconnected neurons; one synchrony of neurons might translate to your idea of the Eiffel tower, for instance, while another, perhaps overlapping, network might represent Paris more generally.

Quietly, over the past couple of decades, neuroscientists have begun to find ways to crack that code. Early steps were made in the 1990s by Theodore Berger at the University of Southern California, who turned to a technique called multi-input/multi-output. MIMO is more typically used to tease signal from noise in wireless communications, but Berger realised he could apply the same principle to pick out meaningful signals from the noise of millions of neurons firing. The quest didn't endear him to sceptics. "People called him crazy for a long, long time," says Eric Leuthardt, a neurosurgeon at Washington University in St Louis, Missouri.

Neural algorithm

It's not that memory signatures have been invisible to other scientists. Some evidence suggests that people have extremely specialised neurons that fire in response to a single concept, such as their grandmother or Jennifer Aniston.

However, these so-called grandmother cells encode a narrow range of ideas, whereas Berger was chasing the ability to encode any memory. Slowly but surely he has shown that the MIMO algorithm can do this – by using it to isolate the specific signal behind the memory of an action, and then replaying that exact sequence.

In one groundbreaking experiment, Berger – now working with Deadwyler and Hampson – implanted a chip containing electrodes into the hippocampus of rats. Then they used the MIMO algorithm to isolate and record the relevant neural code as trained animals pressed one of two levers to receive a treat. After drugging the rats to impair their ability to remember which lever gave the treat, the team then used the same electrodes to deliver the same firing pattern back to the neurons. Despite its amnesia, the rodent knew which lever to push. In other words, the algorithm had helped to restore the rat's lost memory.

It was a triumph, demonstrating that electronics can crack the neural code and potentially replace damaged areas of the brain – acting as an artificial hippocampus to treat amnesia, for instance.

Further developments should allow these neural chips to tackle more sophisticated problems than simple skill learning. "Think of the guy coming back from war who can't remember his wife's face," says Sanchez. For that kind of recognition, the brain breaks down the person, place or object into specific features – such as the colour of their hair or their height – and encodes them separately.

Using MIMO to replicate that process is an ambitious challenge that Deadwyler and Hampson have begun to explore. For instance, they trained macaques to remember the position and shape of a picture on a screen, and then choose the same image from a much larger selection nearly a minute later. All the while the algorithm, via electrodes in the macaques' brains, recorded the neural signals that formed in the prefrontal cortex and hippocampus. Then they drugged the monkeys to disrupt their ability to form new long-term memories, before getting them to perform the task again. When they electrically stimulated neurons with the same signals that they had recorded on successful trials, those monkeys performed a lot better. By injecting the code, they had stimulated the hippocampus and the prefrontal cortex to reproduce the "correct" memories.

Intriguingly, Deadwyler and Hampson had found patterns that corresponded not to the exact images the monkeys were looking at, but to more universal features in them, such as whether they contained the colour blue, or a human face. "This is how we think memory works," says Deadwyler: instead of wastefully creating separate neural signatures for every new person, place or thing you encounter, the brain breaks the incoming information down into features. "Then to remember a specific item, you don't need to remember everything about it," he says. Rather than the fine details, it's the combination of features that help bring the item in question back to mind.

The monkeys' own brain plasticity may have helped, says Daofen Chen at the National Institutes of Health in Bethesda, Maryland. "The brain tries to meet the machine halfway," he says. "It is an adaptive process. Give the brain enough – even imperfect – information, and it can translate it into something it finds useful." This phenomenon has already been robustly demonstrated for cochlear implants, and it could be a powerful aid to any brain-injured people hoping to use future cognitive implants. ❯

One key question raised by Deadwyler's research was whether we each have a different neural code, or whether there is a more generalised language shared by everyone. This is where Deadwyler and Hampson's attempts to transplant memories between rats comes in. Their experiments typically involved two sets of rats trained to run between two arenas, pressing a series of levers in a certain order. Importantly, one set was trained to delay their actions – they had to pause for up to 30 seconds before they were able to press one of the levers – while the second set was not. Presented with the unexpected delay, the second set of rats lost the plot – they could not remember which lever they had been taught to press. But when Deadwyler and Hampson used MIMO to record the brain activity for this task in the first group and replayed it in the second using electrodes, those rats began to act as if they had taken the alternative form of training, choosing the correct lever even after a long pause, even though that had not been part of their previous experiences. "Our model lets us establish a memory that has not been used before," Hampson says.

Was the set-up really this good? Or could their success be explained by some other cause? Deadwyler and Hampson embarked on an enormous number of control experiments to rule out every other explanation, including the possibility that it was just an unintentional artefact of electronically tickling the brain, or some general improvement caused by electrical stimulation. Finally, in December 2013 the paper was published: it really is possible to plant a general signature of a memory in the brain.

Wired up

If that could be replicated in humans, a chip could come with ready-made code that could give people a head start on relearning general skills such as brushing your teeth or driving a car, say – actions that are often lost after brain damage. "Before we can get someone with brain damage back to work, we want to return their capability to form those fundamental declarative memories," says Justin Sanchez, previously in charge of neuroprosthetics research at the University of Miami in Florida.

As the technology improves, brain chips that incorporate electrodes and algorithms like MIMO may be able to translate extremely fine details of an experience. Ranulfo Romo at the National Autonomous University of Mexico has shown that his chips can pick up the signals that capture very subtle changes in sensory perceptions, such as a certain frequency of vibrations against the skin. As a proof of principle, he even used the set-up to implant one monkey's ongoing sensations into another's brain, as if they were telepathic. "The monkeys integrated the false perception as their own working memory," says Romo.

Whose memory?

The work is an important sign of the recent progress, says John Donoghue of Brown University in Providence, Rhode Island, whose work on brain-machine interfaces inspired current neuroengineering. "The monkey had to make a sophisticated perceptual distinction," he says. "Romo showed that not only do you detect the information, but you can use it as if it were real," he says.

Such fine-tuned decoding of sensory information could have important applications beyond restoring perceptual information to memories. For instance, sometimes people lose the ability to speak thanks to damage in the brain between Wernicke's area and Broca's area. A chip capable of picking up on those detailed sensory signals and translating them between the two regions might therefore return their speech.

Despite these advances, the biggest unknown is the quality of the experiences. "For an animal, you can't ask them 'what is your perception of a memory?'," says Sanchez. That could soon change. The Restoring Active Memory project, run by Sanchez for the US Defense Advanced Research Projects Agency (DARPA), is pushing the research towards human studies. It is backing two teams – one led by researchers at the University of California, Los Angeles, and the other led by the University of Pennsylvania – and one of the first steps will be to understand how the experience of a new memory translates into electrical code in the human brain.

Prying into the hippocampus is already a familiar undertaking, thanks mostly to experiments on people with intractable epilepsy, whose doctors eavesdrop on their brain signals using deep penetrating electrodes to better understand their condition (see "Source code", page 114). MIMO, Sanchez says, is only one of several

Rebuilding broken brains

Electronic implants could help people with brain damage by recording neural signals and then relaying them around the damaged area

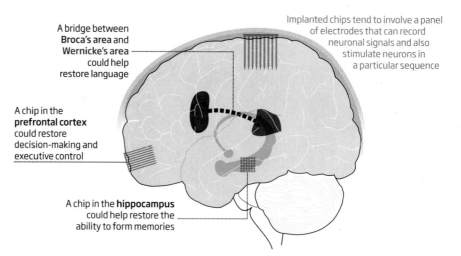

A bridge between **Broca's area** and **Wernicke's area** could help restore language

Implanted chips tend to involve a panel of electrodes that can record neuronal signals and also stimulate neurons in a particular sequence

A chip in the **prefrontal cortex** could restore decision-making and executive control

A chip in the **hippocampus** could help restore the ability to form memories

contenders for processing these signals. After the competing algorithms and electronics have been tested and refined on volunteers like these, prototype chips will enter clinical trials. These studies will require the approval of the US Food and Drug Administration and informed consent of the volunteers. If deemed sufficiently safe by the FDA, a chip will be cleared for use. DARPA hopes to use the resulting implants to help soldiers who return from war with traumatic brain injuries.

Several neuroengineering researchers envision similar chips for people with

"Activate the right circuits, and you generate the illusion that you are recalling something"

Alzheimer's disease and stroke, depending on the extent of the damage. In more severe cases of brain damage, Hampson imagines a device worn on the belt, with buttons that help you remember specific locations and their meanings. "Let's say I'm in the kitchen – I need to remember where the silverware is," he says. The patient would press the right button "and the memory pops up because we've stored the code".

As the target population for such implants widens, the obvious ethical questions centre around issues of informed consent. After all, for most experimental procedures, consent

requires a sound mind, and memory chips are specific interventions for people whose minds have been damaged. Both Deadwyler and Sanchez say this issue is more straightforward than it appears: procedures have long been in place to allow close relatives of people in comas or with illnesses such as Alzheimer's to make decisions for them.

The deeper questions about memory modification were familiar staples in the arts long before Neo uploaded kung fu. As the famous film-maker Luis Buñuel put it: "Our memory is our coherence, our reason, our feeling, even our action. Without it, we are nothing." If you change those memories artificially, are you still you?

Deadwyler and Hampson's rat experiments highlight one possible concern: your memories may no longer be your own. "Activate the right circuits, and you generate the illusion that you are recalling something," says Romo. What kind of controls could ensure that every implanted memory reflected the reality of that person's environment? And whether or not those memories are your own, sparking neurons related to memory will eventually lead, directly or not, to changes in your decisions – so who is responsible for the consequences of those decisions?

There is also the chance that such chips could resurrect long-buried events. Not all of those recollections will be wanted – one of the brain's biggest talents is to forget, as well as to remember. But perhaps it's a small price to pay for a lifetime of new memories to come. ∎

32 MILE ELECTRIC RANGE

148 MPG

510 MILE COMBINED RANGE

ULTRA LOW CO$_2$ EMISSIONS

44 G/KM

MITSUBISHI MOTORS

INTELLIGENT MOTION

WE HAVEN'T JUST MADE HISTORY
WE'RE SAVING DRIVERS £1,000s

The Mitsubishi Outlander PHEV is cutting costs across the country – and if you're one of Britain's average daily drivers you can use just a few drops of petrol each day.

This intelligent hybrid decides when it's more efficient to use petrol or electricity, giving it the ability to deliver a staggering 148mpg[1]. With an electric range of up to 32 miles the Outlander PHEV easily tackles the UK's average daily drive on a single charge – and on longer journeys the petrol engine helps out to achieve a combined range of up to 510 miles[2]. The battery can be charged in just a few hours via a domestic plug socket[3], a low-cost home Charge Point[4] or one of over 7,500 Charge Points found across the UK. With ultra-low CO$_2$ emissions the Outlander PHEV is exempt from Road Tax and the London Congestion Charge[5] – as well as being eligible for drastically reduced Benefit in Kind taxation[6]. There's even £5,000 off the list price through the Government Plug-in Car Grant, which means an Outlander PHEV will cost you from just £28,249[7], the same price as the Outlander Diesel – and it comes with a 5 year warranty[8].

We've made history, you just need to make time to find out how we can save you £1,000s.
We call this Intelligent Motion.

MITSUBISHI
OUTLANDER PHEV
THE UK's FAVOURITE PLUG-IN HYBRID

FROM £28,249 - £39,999

Including £5,000 Government Plug-in Car Grant[7]

Discover how. Search PHEV. | Visit: mitsubishi-cars.co.uk to find your nearest dealer

1. Official EU MPG test figure shown as a guide for comparative purposes and may not reflect real driving results. 2. 32 mile EV range achieved with full battery charge. 510 miles achieved with combined full battery and petrol tank. Actual range will vary depending on driving style and road conditions. 3. Domestic plug charge: 5 hours, 16 Amp home charge point: 3.5 hours, 80% rapid charge: 30mins. 4. Government subsidised charge points are available from a number of suppliers for a small fee - ask your dealer for more information. 5. Congestion Charge application required, subject to administrative fee. 6. 5% BIK compared to the average rate of 25%. 7. Prices shown include the Government Plug-in Car Grant and VAT (at 20%), but **exclude First Registration Fee**. Model shown is an Outlander PHEV GX4h at £33,399 including the Government Plug-in Car Grant and metallic paint. On The Road prices range from £28,304.00 to £40,054.00 and include VED, First Registration Fee and the Government Plug-in Car Grant. **Metallic/pearlescent paint extra**. Prices correct at time of going to print. For more information about the Government Plug-in Car Grant please visit www.gov.uk/plug-in-car-van-grants. 8. All new Outlander PHEV variants come with a 5 year/62,500 mile warranty (whichever occurs first), for more information please visit www.mitsubishi-cars.co.uk/warranty

Outlander PHEV range fuel consumption in mpg (ltrs/100km): Full Battery Charge: no fuel used, Depleted Battery Charge: 48mpg (5.9), Weighted Average: 148mpg (1.9), CO$_2$ Emissions: 44 g/km.

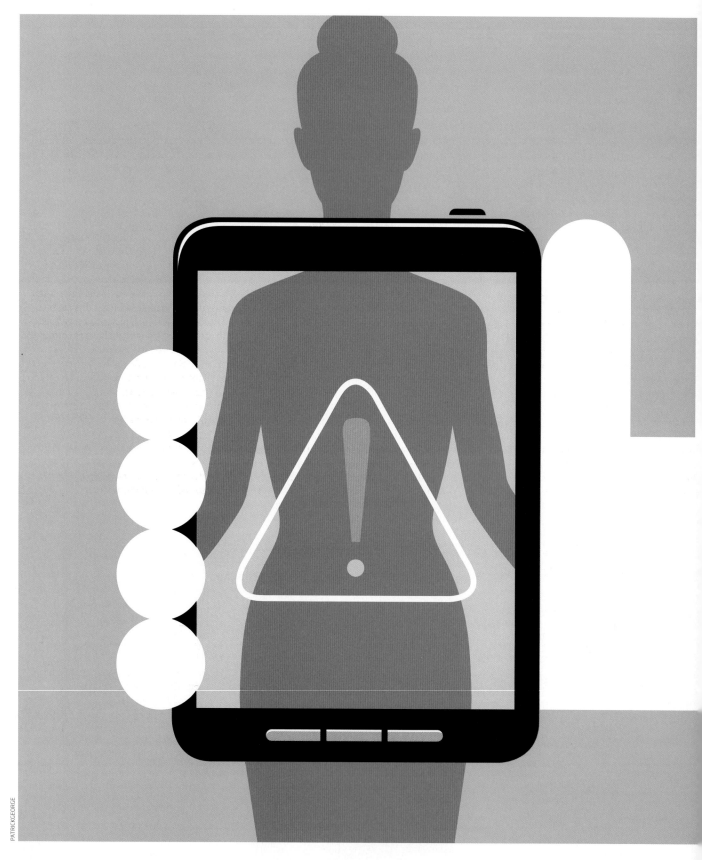

HAZEL – as we'll call her – knew something was wrong when, in her mid-50s, she started to feel short of breath at the slightest exertion. Over the next few months, she felt increasingly achy, but several medical visits and an X-ray suggested only arthritis. More troubling symptoms appeared: a persistent cough, a sore knee and tender lungs.

Whether we have had to deal with worrying symptoms or not, at some point we have all found ourselves, like Hazel, wondering what's happening inside our own bodies. Maybe you want to know whether that cough will become a garden-variety cold or debilitating flu, or whether your child has an ear infection. At present, the only way to find out is to see a doctor. What if there were a gadget that could offer a reliable home diagnosis?

Such a device could be in your hands sooner than you think. In 2012, the X Prize Foundation partnered with communications giant Qualcomm to launch a $10 million competition to develop a pocket medical diagnostic tool, to be ready to demonstrate on humans in mid-2015. And in September 2014, 10 finalists were announced. The contest's organisers say they want to usher in a new era of medical technology, one that would revolutionise healthcare in the face of spiralling costs and, in the US, a steady fall in the number of doctors providing primary care. But just how many of a physician's complex duties can be turned over to technology?

Peter Diamandis of the X Prize Foundation said in 2012 that the guidelines were inspired by the "medical tricorder" featured in the TV series *Star Trek*. Waved like a wand over the human body, the smartphone-like device was capable of diagnosing myriad ailments.

Like the tricorder, the winning device must be portable, weighing no more than 2.25 kilograms. It must be able to diagnose 12 specific medical conditions – ranging from a common ear infection to pneumonia – and monitor five vital signs (see diagram, page 120). Competing teams must also choose three from a list of 12 more ambitious "elective" conditions to detect, including melanoma, food poisoning and HIV infection.

The guidelines specify that devices that work in the least invasive way will score best with the judges – a panel of non-expert users. And unlike the box of tricks on the TV show, competition devices must make diagnoses without any help from medical professionals.

Can handheld gadgets do all this? If the enthusiastic response to the competition is anything to go by, they soon will. Before the competition had even launched, over 260 teams had unofficially preregistered, reflecting the fact that many of the components needed to build such a device already exist. Sensors have become powerful, small and cheap; high-resolution touchscreens are ubiquitous in phones and tablets; and cloud computing offers powerful number-crunching capabilities and access to vast online data stores.

Smartphones can already make startlingly sensitive measurements. With the right app installed, a phone can monitor your heart rate – one of the vital signs in the contest guidelines – simply by using the camera to illuminate and count the pulse in your finger. Another handheld device, the Scout, to be released later this year by contest finalist Scanadu – a NASA spin-off based in Moffett Field, California – can measure four of the five vital signs on the competition's list simply by being held to the forehead.

Inspector gadget

Monitoring vital signs is one thing. But detecting many of the conditions on the list requires bodily fluids to be analysed. Some competitors say they can do this. The ScanaFlo, another device Scanadu is developing, allows a smartphone to analyse urine using a small immunoassay paddle, which is dipped into the fluid to be tested. If proteins associated with disease are present, it changes colour, which can be analysed by an app to make a diagnosis. Walter De Brouwer, Scanadu's CEO, says it is even possible to collect and test blood with a smartphone attachment consisting of a patch of nanoneedles that are painless to use.

All this strains the definition of "non-invasive", but two emerging technologies could make it unnecessary to involve bodily fluids at all.

Some conditions can be revealed simply by the sound of your voice. Researchers at ▶

Could a handheld gadget that can accurately diagnose disease soon be a reality? **Phil McKenna** investigates

The doctor is in your pocket

The doctor in a box

$10 million in prize money is on offer in an international contest to build a handheld gadget that anyone can use to diagnose disease

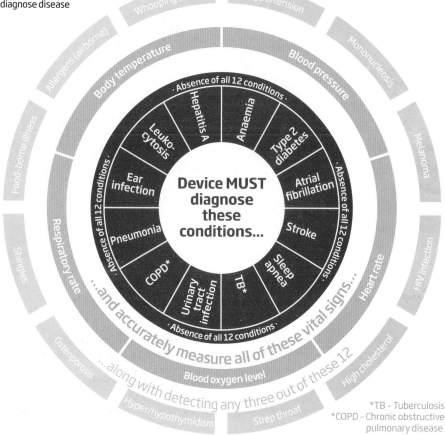

Body temperature
Whooping cough
Hypertension
Allergens (airborne)
Blood pressure
Mononucleosis
Melanoma
Food-borne illness
HIV infection
Respiratory rate
Heart rate
Shingles
Osteoporosis
High cholesterol
Hyper/hypothyroidism
Blood oxygen level
Strep throat

Device MUST diagnose these conditions...

...and accurately measure all of these vital signs...

...along with detecting any three out of these 12

Absence of all 12 conditions
Hepatitis A
Anaemia
Leuko-cytosis
Type 2 diabetes
Ear infection
Atrial fibrillation
Pneumonia
Stroke
COPD*
Sleep apnea
Urinary tract infection
TB*
Absence of all 12 conditions
Absence of all 12 conditions
Absence of all 12 conditions

*TB – Tuberculosis
*COPD – Chronic obstructive pulmonary disease

the University of Oxford demonstrated in 2012 that Parkinson's disease can be detected by voice-analysis software: the same tremors, weakness and rigidity that affect the limbs of Parkinson's patients also affect the vocal cords. In laboratory tests, the software could detect the presence or absence of the disease with 99 per cent accuracy. What's more, another study found that this vocal impairment could be detected up to five years before clinical diagnosis. Voice analysis will go far beyond Parkinson's, says Max Little, who heads the initiative: it could also diagnose other conditions on the X Prize lists, including sleep apnea, whooping cough and stroke.

But voice analysis pales in comparison to what we might find by taking a closer look at what we exhale. In 2013, researchers at the Swiss Federal Institute of Technology in Zurich revealed that all of us have unique "breathprints" that may serve as a diagnostic tool. This field has been advancing rapidly. "Twenty years ago we knew breath contained a lot of stuff but we didn't know what biomarkers corresponded to what diseases,"

says Cristina Davis, a bioinstrumentation expert at the University of California, Davis. "We can detect things now that 10 years ago you couldn't measure."

Bad breath

Breath analysis can, in principle, be used to diagnose tuberculosis, chronic obstructive pulmonary disease (COPD), pneumonia and diabetes, all on the competition's main list. And researchers at the Cleveland Clinic in Ohio showed in 2013 that breath tests could detect lung cancer with 75 to 80 per cent accuracy – on a par with that of a CT scan, the standard way to make the diagnosis – even before symptoms developed. "That might be early enough that it can be found at a curable stage," says Peter Mazzone, head of Cleveland Clinic's research on breath analysis for lung cancer detection.

Had Hazel been able to access such testing at home, her condition might have been diagnosed more readily. She endured nearly three years of steadily worsening symptoms, including skin that turned purple under her

husband's touch and hurt so much the pain made her jump. Finally, she sought a second opinion. "My physician wasn't connecting the dots," she said. By the time her new doctor referred her to specialists, what had started as lung cancer had spread to her liver, bones and brain. She was told she might have six months to live. Hazel was adamant that a simple home test would have been invaluable for her. "If I'd had a tool that could detect cancer, I would immediately have gone for a second opinion," she said at the time.

But even if handheld diagnostic gadgets were available, and all the sensors did their job perfectly, detecting a chemical is not the same thing as diagnosing a disease. How will such devices avoid false positives or negatives?

False positives could cause a lot of emotional harm, says Michael Epton at Christchurch Hospital in New Zealand. When making a diagnosis based on trace chemical compounds in our breath, for instance, the risk is significant. In 2009, Epton's team found that a chemical signature they had attributed to COPD was actually produced by the asthma inhalers that people with the condition often used. "You have to train sensors to make sure you are detecting a specific disease," Epton says. "You don't want the machine to cry wolf."

And as Hazel's experience illustrates, the repercussions of a false negative can be even worse. To prevent false negatives, the competition guidelines say that devices must accurately diagnose an "absence of conditions" – in other words, if the user does not have any of the 12 conditions that devices must be able to detect, then the diagnosis must say so with a high level of certainty.

Competitors could find themselves walking a fine line between false positives and negatives. HIV testing, one of the elective conditions, will be especially challenging, says Anna Mastroianni, a law professor at the University of Washington in Seattle. At the moment, HIV tests in the US, whether in a clinic or at home, must be vetted by a doctor who acts as a "learned intermediary", protecting the test-kit maker from liability in the case of an incorrect result. By having a device which is supposed to be used independently of a doctor, the contest guidelines are effectively removing that middleman. "What kind of liability does the manufacturer have?" Mastroianni says.

Granted, if your tricorder gives you a false positive, a doctor's visit is likely to clear up the misunderstanding. The problem is that a false negative may not prompt similar vigilance.

Uneasy tensions like these may explain why teasing conclusions from the subtleties of symptoms has traditionally been left to medical professionals. "Doctors practise, they learn, there is some finesse involved," says Jill Smith, an emergency room nurse in Baltimore, Maryland.

Self diagnosis

Smith says a tricorder of sorts is already being used and the results are not all that promising. "It's called Dr Google," she says. The problem is that people trawl the web for medical information, and then often either overestimate or underestimate the significance of their symptoms. "They'll say, 'oh, I only have six out of seven signs of a heart attack; I'm fine,'" and then we don't see them until it's too late," she says. Even though a tricorder would perform tests to make a diagnosis, Smith says it cannot replace a physician's training. "Until you have a computer that can reason based on things it has learned," she says, "I don't think you can take the art out of medicine."

However, artificial intelligence techniques could help close that gap. In recent years, AI has made vast leaps in its ability to tease conclusions out of massive data troves. Pedro Domingos, a computer scientist at the University of Washington in Seattle, says the AI needed to back up a successful tricorder will probably resemble Watson, the IBM supercomputer that famously beat the human champions on the US quiz show *Jeopardy!*. IBM is currently honing Watson's medical knowledge and working with several US hospitals to develop a virtual nurse.

A Watson-like tricorder would access the latest medical literature to inform its diagnoses. "There is more medical knowledge than doctors can keep up with today, and your tricorder will be able to access that," Domingos says. AI would also be able to cope with what he calls "fuzzy evidence". No single measurement is usually sufficient to predict a given disease, he says: "It's the combination

of them." So a Bayesian network – a type of probabilistic learning AI that can determine the chances of someone having a disease based on their symptoms – will likely be included in the winning design. It will also be able to learn from experience. "It can generalise beyond symptoms it has seen and learn to diagnose similar cases, not just what it has previously seen."

Perhaps the final frontier for a tricorder would be acquiring a supportive bedside manner. "Talking to a box would be a cold relationship," says Kim Ayscue, a former nurse who is now a professor of nursing at Lynchburg College in Virginia. "Many people, especially those with chronic, long-term diseases, want more of the psychological, social side of medicine, and that is the art of being a healthcare provider."

Even here, AI could step in. With the right natural-language user interface, a tricorder would sound genuinely sympathetic, Domingos says. "You can imagine [Apple's digital personal assistant] Siri having a

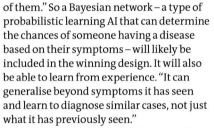

"There is more medical knowledge than doctors can keep up with – but a tricorder could access it"

medical side to it; 'you seem depressed. Are you congested? Do you have a runny nose?'"

With costly diagnostic equipment and procedures fuelling a rapid rise in the cost of care, a medical tricorder cannot come soon enough for some people. In 2011, the US alone spent $2.7 trillion on healthcare, equivalent to nearly one-fifth of its economic output, up from less than one-tenth 30 years ago. "The medical system is so bloated and stuck in its ways that it will take disruptive technology like this to change the status quo," says Catherine Brownstein, an epidemiologist at Boston Children's Hospital. "It could make expensive diagnostic systems obsolete."

With an array of different devices in the final, the competition should at least improve the situation. Some will analyse blood samples, others will rely on asking a series of questions, while others will analyse breath and take pictures. Judging will take place at the end of 2015, with the winners announced the following year.

But as Hazel's story suggests, we could all bear in mind that sometimes no diagnosis is bulletproof, whether made by a machine or a human. Hazel died a little over a year after she was told she had six months to live, and maybe a tricorder would have done no better than her physician. But it's early days and technology is advancing fast. "I think a medical tricorder would be helpful, if only to have as a monitor if you suspect something," she told me. "I thought something was strange. I had no idea what it was, and I wasn't getting answers from anyone else." ■

BY MY fourth interview, I'd developed a checklist to use before each meeting. For starters, I would make sure I had grown some hair. I'd also check that I was fully clothed – I had learned the hard way about that one. Only then would I teleport to the interview, hoping that this time my avatar wouldn't materialise in anyone's lap.

That was in Second Life, a virtual world that at its peak had around 20 million players globally. In it, the avatars – digital stand-ins for the players – create everything around them. Every cobbled street, every tree swaying in the wind, even the wind itself, is the product of someone's imagination.

For many users, though, Second Life became much more than a game. The ability to construct and control a virtual environment led to the creation of, among other things, a new branch of psychotherapy – avatar therapy – in which therapists interact with their clients avatar to avatar.

On the face of it, this might sound like a pale imitation of a real-life therapy session. Yet its proponents say avatar therapy has some unique advantages that take psychotherapy to a different level. In a virtual world, therapy sessions are not confined to a virtual office; they can also involve role-play scenarios to allow the patient to practise their newly learned coping skills in virtual environments tailored to their needs. All the while the

therapist gives real-time feedback, like a medically qualified Jiminy Cricket.

Launched in 2003, Second Life was one of the first virtual worlds known as massively multiplayer online games. It was designed not for fighting monsters, but for people to socialise and, increasingly, emulate real life. Musicians have concerts, artists display their work and scientists go to meetings. And over time, people have found ways to work, learn and connect in these virtual worlds. So can they be used for therapy too?

As a technophile, I love the idea; as a psychotherapist used to working the old-fashioned way, I had reservations. So I decided to meet some of the advocates of virtual therapy in their own domain, avatar to avatar, to see if they could address my concerns.

One of my first interviews was with Dick Dillon, who started out as a mental health counsellor and now runs Innovaision, a company that builds virtual therapy platforms. In Second Life, Dillon's avatar is a bald, square-jawed hunk with a passing resemblance to Bruce Willis. He took me through a typical session.

At a certain stage of therapy, you and your therapist may have come to the decision, for example, that it is time to revisit the site of a traumatic event – a car crash, say. But in real life it is too far away, or perhaps you don't yet feel happy

THE VIRTUAL THERAPIST WILL SEE YOU NOW

Can the connection between therapist and client be replicated in cyberspace? Samantha Murphy investigates

driving. No problem: your therapist builds, or "rezzes", the scene in a matter of minutes. Soon you are driving on a familiar road, with a steep bend similar to the one that you lost control on in the rain. As you approach the turn, your anxiety increases and your breaths become faster. The therapist coaches you, reminding you of symptom-management techniques. If it all becomes too much, they instantly zap you back into the office.

This set-up lets the therapist give real-time feedback while providing an experience that feels genuine, yet takes place in the safe environment of a simulation. The emotions are real. The rewards are real. Only the location is fake.

"When the brain sees a 3D object in real life it converts it to a 2D object in the visual cortex," says Jeremy Bailenson, head of the Virtual Human Interaction Lab at Stanford University in California. Perhaps that's why a virtual scene can still provoke a strong psychological reaction, he says.

Phobia exposure

One of the first applications of avatar therapy was in treating social anxiety disorder, a crippling shyness that can confine people to their homes. James Herbert, head of the anxiety treatment and research programme at Drexel University in Philadelphia, Pennsylvania, was among the first wave of researchers to investigate avatar therapy. Encouragingly, clients generally rated the treatment highly, though there were exceptions. "Some patients and therapists reported frustration with not being able to see the individual's face," he says, and sometimes technical difficulties interrupted the sessions.

Avatar therapy has also helped people with phobias. In real life, the usual treatment is to gradually expose people to the source of their fear, but this can sometimes be difficult. An avatar therapist can introduce the phobia source while remaining in complete control, scaling the experience up or down according to the client's reaction.

In fact, many of the conditions treated by face-to-face talk therapy can also be treated virtually, including depression and anxiety. Avatar therapy is proving useful for more diverse conditions too, such as traumatic brain injury, schizophrenia and Asperger's syndrome. So far studies have shown similar success rates to traditional therapy for social anxiety, post-traumatic stress disorder and drug and alcohol addiction.

SECOND LIFE

In the virtual world, counselling sessions need not be confined to the therapist's office

"The emotions are real. The rewards are real. Only the location is fake"

What about the downsides of avatar therapy – doesn't it lack the personal touch? "A real therapist dealing with a real person is more likely to feel ethical responsibility and care for that patient," says Christine Webber, a psychotherapist based in London.

The other major concern is the loss of body language. For people used to virtual worlds, this is not as much of a problem as you might think, according to Dillon. But as a therapist, I glean a great deal from seeing someone become tearful or shift in their seat.

It's a trade-off, say avatar therapists. What you lose in body language you gain in the eloquent expression of conscious thought – at least for clients who type in their responses – as well as the loss of inhibition that comes with communicating through an avatar.

For people seeking therapy online, there are practical concerns, too: how can they be sure the people offering treatment are bona fide therapists, for example, and how can you be sure you are talking confidentially? "Second Life, as a commercial, open-enrolment game environment, is too public," says Dillon. "It would be like having a therapy session at Starbucks." Therapists who use this approach prefer to create bespoke secure virtual spaces in which to work.

So are psychotherapists ready to leave some of their most basic tools behind? "It's not for everyone," says Kelli Turgyan, a social worker practising in Lancaster, Pennsylvania. "This type of therapy would have to be done by the right type of therapist for the right type of client." Because of the lack of face-to-face contact, only low-risk clients should be taken on, she says.

That might change as the technology becomes more sophisticated. In one notable study in 2013, avatar therapy helped people with schizophrenia cope with auditory hallucinations, or hearing voices. Participants created an avatar for the voice and were encouraged to confront and challenge it, with the voice's "responses" controlled by the therapist. Many participants reported that their voices became less threatening or abusive, or less frequent, and in one case the voice disappeared completely.

It is early days, and the technology is not without its pitfalls, but this form of therapy is gaining converts. There's no official head count, but more and more therapists are now offering virtual services. You could say avatar therapy is virtually there. ■

WHEN June slipped on an icy pavement and fractured her wrist, the doctors treating her thought little of it. She was a fit and healthy 65-year-old. Her wrist was set in a cast and she was sent home. But two years later, June tripped in the garden and couldn't get up. She was still there the following morning, when her son found her and took her to hospital.

June had osteoporosis. She had fractured a bone in her hip and needed major surgery to put in an artificial replacement. She later suffered two fractures to her vertebrae, deforming her spine and restricting her breathing. Confined to bed for six weeks, she developed a chest infection and died.

Her case is not unusual. Osteoporosis, where bones become weak and fragile, is often missed first time round. But by 2018, such an experience could be entirely different. After that initial fracture, June's bone density would be measured and she'd be sent home wearing sensors that continuously recorded her activity levels, gait and posture. She'd be offered a CT scan to capture the exact structure of her bones and reveal areas of wear, tear or weakness. All of this data would then be plugged into a computer simulation that would create a virtual June, fast-forward her through the years, and predict her physical destiny.

A medically accurate digital double could revolutionise your life, finds **Linda Geddes**

IN SICKNESS
AND
IN HEALTH

Welcome to the Virtual Physiological Human, an initiative backed by the European Union that has attracted £200 million of investment and more than 2000 researchers. The next decade is already set to bring personalised drugs and diagnoses based on a growing mass of patient data, covering everything from lifestyle to genetic profile. But the Virtual Physiological Human project has an even bigger goal in its sights.

In the 2020s, each of us could grow a kind of twin. Detailed simulations of the inner workings of our bodies, from the interactions of genes and proteins in individual cells up to organs and whole-body systems, will be combined with data about our medical histories and the kind of lives we lead. The result will be a digital body double that could be experimented on, testing outcomes for different drugs, surgical interventions and lifestyle choices. We would go through life with a virtual clone.

"Finally, we will be able to say something about you," says Marco Viceconti at the University of Sheffield, UK. "Not because you are the same age, or sex, or have the same genetic profile and disease as a thousand other people, but because you are you with your condition, your history, your bad habits." With power handed to each of us, healthcare as we know it would be turned on its head. Armed with a personal health forecast, we can choose to take charge of our health rather than accept our fate. But a glimpse of the future brings a responsibility to act. How will we cope?

Embracing complexity

The Virtual Physiological Human initiative sprang from a 2005 summit at which European researchers from many different areas of bioengineering, physiology and clinical medicine agreed that a common pattern was emerging. Trying to tackle diseases by breaking them down into smaller parts and then looking at each one individually was no longer working. "If you look at the big diseases that plague Western society – cardiovascular disease, cancer, diabetes, osteoporosis – the one thing they have in common is that their symptoms cannot be explained by looking at one part of the body," says Viceconti.

Take osteoporosis. We know that many fractures in elderly people are the result of reduced bone density, and that this is caused by a hormone-related shift in the activities of different bone cells. But fragile bones are only part of the story. Deteriorating eyesight or

hearing, weaker muscles, a person's activity levels and posture all increase the risk of falling and fracturing bones.

A pure focus on genetics doesn't tell you that much about your future risk of developing these complex conditions. "You can have a genomic blueprint, but it will not tell you precisely what's going to come out at higher organisational levels," says Peter Coveney at University College London.

Doctors caring for patients with multiple conditions, such as diabetes and heart failure together, face a similar problem. "The links between different diseases aren't always made," says Liesbet Geris at the University of Liège in Belgium. "It's often hard to envisage what the effect of medication for the heart problem will be on the diabetes, or how these two diseases will interact."

In short, we have reached a point where it is no longer possible to ignore complexity. We have to embrace it. That was the conclusion of those researchers who met back in 2005. And their solution? Build computer models that can combine the vast amounts of data about biological processes at the smallest scale – the workings of genes, proteins, and cells – with our growing understanding of whole-body systems. The models would simulate how the body's microscopic machinery gives rise to everything else. This can then be integrated with a patient's personal data, ultimately creating virtual models of us all.

Already, researchers have produced digital models of major organs like the heart and liver, which can be used to design new drugs. They can even model the forces generated by blood flowing through the arteries in a person's brain, and predict whether an area of weakness known as an aneurysm is likely to rupture and cause a stroke. So far, most of these models aim to give a real-time window on activity in the present, rather than predict the future. But that is coming.

Viceconti and his colleagues have developed an osteoporosis model designed to second- ❯

"Finally, we can say something about you: your condition, your history, your bad habits"

TOMMY PARKER

"If you have a virtual patient, you could select the treatment with the highest cure rate and the lowest toxic effect"

guess an individual's risk of sustaining a fracture, by combining existing patient data with CT scans and information from wearable sensors. The goal is that by 2018, people like June whose osteoporosis may be relatively mild, yet have a high risk of fracturing bones because they are more likely to fall over, could be better identified. "This would allow us to not only target therapies that would protect their skeleton, but design exercise interventions to address an individual's risk of falling," says Eugene McCloskey at the University of Sheffield, who is also working on the bone fracture model.

Other teams are studying the musculoskeletal system too. Geris, for example, has been using computer simulations to try to speed-up the development of tissue implants to heal bone fractures. She has modelled the process of bone growth from the bottom up, starting with the interaction between different genes to identify the key proteins that influence cell growth. The simulations can then predict how adding different chemical factors might influence fracture healing at the level of the whole bone. "It's all about trying to make better decisions than the ones we've made through trial and error in the past," says Geris.

The complete patient

One big challenge facing researchers is figuring out how to hook all these systems together into a complete patient. For now, they remain a collection of disembodied parts. But we may not be far off. For example, Robert Hester at the University of Mississippi Medical Center in Jackson and his colleagues have developed a mathematical model of the whole body called HumMod. It contains some 5000 variables that describe factors including measurements of blood flow, recordings of heart and brain activity, results of blood tests and scans of our bones, muscles and organs, as well as features of the environment, such as air temperature and humidity. Tweaking the numbers lets you play out potential scenarios for particular patients.

Maths is only part of the puzzle, though. Models like HumMod will then need to be stitched together with an ever-growing mountain of biochemical and physical simulations, personal histories of illness and injury, and descriptions of diet and lifestyle. The goal is for Virtual Physiological Human models to be able to integrate different types of patient information – MRI scans and genetic data, say – quickly and automatically, even in emergency scenarios (see diagram, left).

But for a doctor or nurse to run such simulations on demand will require more computing power than most hospitals have at their disposal. Indeed, several researchers, such as Coveney, who models blood flow in the brain, currently run their simulations on a supercomputer. "If you ask me point blank who is using modelling and simulation to save people's lives, there's very little of it at the moment," says Coveney. Yet the wheels are turning. The US Food and Drug Administration, for example, is already considering large-scale simulations for drug testing.

The toughest challenges are unlikely to be technical, however. For starters, there could be resistance from the medical community who may feel their scope for judgement is being taken away.

The hope, though, is that doctors will be more confident that the treatments they offer will improve patients' health. "At the moment, doctors often have just one chance to get it right," says Norbert Graf, a medical director at Saarland University Hospital in Germany. "But if you have a virtual patient, you could select the treatment with the highest cure rate and the lowest toxic effect." Doctors would still need to speak to the patient, make the diagnosis, and select and administer the treatment – but they'd have another tool at their disposal. "The difference is that there would now be a model selecting which is the best treatment for the individual patient, not a protocol that is the same for hundreds of patients," says Graf.

Having a virtual twin should make us pay more attention to our own well-being, putting responsibility for healthcare into our hands, say researchers behind the project. But when it comes to looking after ourselves, our track record is mixed. Not everyone

A dose of your own medicine

By the mid 2020s, we could have virtual twins that can immediately test-run even emergency surgeries to see how we will fare

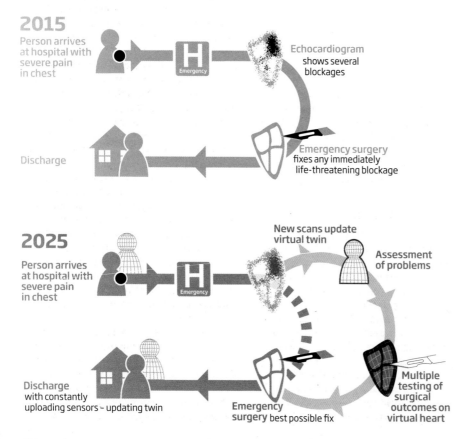

2015

Person arrives at hospital with severe pain in chest

H Emergency

Echocardiogram shows several blockages

Emergency surgery fixes any immediately life-threatening blockage

Discharge

2025

Person arrives at hospital with severe pain in chest

H Emergency

New scans update virtual twin

Assessment of problems

Multiple testing of surgical outcomes on virtual heart

Emergency surgery best possible fix

Discharge with constantly uploading sensors - updating twin

"It's all about trying to make better decisions than the ones we've made in the past"

agrees that this will motivate people to take charge of their health.

Jane Wardle at University College London has investigated the impact that genetic screening for obesity or lung cancer has had on people's motivation to eat healthily or give up smoking. "Giving people more detail about future risk has never produced the effects that people hoped," Wardle says. Often people feel very motivated in the short term. "They say that 'It's a wake-up call'," she says. "However, in the long run, it's not actually achieving any behaviour change."

Even so, those working on virtual versions of us are optimistic. Evidence suggests that being confronted with a vision of your own future – rather than being told you have a 65 per cent chance of developing lung cancer, say – can have a big impact.

"Visual imagery is more emotionally arousing than non-visual information," says Hal Hershfield at New York University. Hershfield is interested in how thinking about our future selves affects our decision-making.

In one recent experiment, he took photos of volunteers and used them to create aged avatars, complete with jowls, bags under the eyes and grey hair. The volunteers then took control of their avatar in a virtual world, where they were confronted by this aged image of themselves in a mirror.

Decisions, decisions

Later, they were given a choice of four ways to spend $1000: buy a gift for someone special, have a party, put the money in a current account, or invest in a retirement fund. Hershfield found that people who came face to face with an older doppelgänger put nearly twice as much into the retirement fund as those who saw an avatar who was the same age as themselves. A related study by Jesse Fox at Ohio State University in Columbus has shown that watching a personalised avatar lose weight by exercising can motivate people to go to the gym within the next 24 hours.

At heart, we're wishful thinkers. Asked

to imagine how we would look and feel if we continue to lead unhealthy lives, it is easy to conjure up a better future than is realistic. Confronting the future seems to help. "Imagination can only go so far," says Hershfield.

But as Wardle points out, the challenge is translating short-term motivational boosts into long-term change. And herein lies another key difference between genetic screening and individualised medicine. As a lifelong companion, the virtual twin would allow us to track our health continuously. Many people already use health apps on their phones to track their diet, exercise and quality of sleep. Adding such data to your simulated self would refine the models and boost their predictive accuracy. "This isn't just a gene saying you have a 90 per cent chance of getting cancer and there's nothing you can do about it," says Geris. "Your genetic profile won't change. But if you change your pattern of behaviour and food intake, the model can update. If you let yourself go, your prognosis will change."

Interventions could also be tailored to specific people like June. By 2025, data from wearable sensors could constantly and automatically update your risk of fracture. New advice based on these updates could then be streamed back to a smartphone. Local weather conditions might be taken into account. If your digital double deemed you were at risk of falling, it could send you a reminder to put on the anti-slip shoes it had encouraged you to buy after noticing that your stability was getting worse.

For some, this may be too much. Ultimately, the biggest roadblock may be our own unease. For the grand vision to work, all of our medical data will need to be put online, an idea that has already met resistance. We may also resent the intrusion of extra surveillance. And then there's the very real possibility that a virtual twin may throw up insights that we are not prepared for, such as a better understanding of how and when we are likely to die. A diagnosis of terminal cancer, for example, leads some to vow to fight it and others to lose the will to go on. Deciding how much we each want to know will need to be decided on a case-by-case basis.

It may be that our virtual twins will need to mirror more than just our biology. "There are different personality traits that are going to predict how people will react to bad news," says Fox. "If you're going to model the physical body, you really need to think about modelling a person's psychological state as well." ■

COMING SOON

NewScientist
THE COLLECTION

VOL TWO / ISSUE THREE

BEING HUMAN

MIND, BODY, SELF, EMOTIONS,
RELATIONSHIPS, POSSESSIONS. THE INSIDE
STORY OF WHAT IT MEANS TO BE ONE OF US

ON SALE 22 JULY

To buy back issues of *New Scientist: The Collection*,
visit *newscientist.com/TheCollection*

One: The Big Questions / Two: Unknown Universe
Three: A Scientific Guide to a Better You / Four: The Human Story
Five: The Human Brain

DARREN HOPES